Digital Transistor Circuits

Semiconductor Electronics Education Committee Books

Digital Transistor Circuits

Semiconductor Electronics Education Committee, Volume 6

J. N. Harris
Lincoln Laboratory
Massachusetts Institute of Technology

P. E. Gray
Massachusetts Institute of Technology

C. L. Searle
Massachusetts Institute of Technology

John Wiley & Sons, Inc., New York · London · Sydney

Foreword

The importance of transistors and other semiconductor devices is now well established. The subsequent development of microminiaturized electronic circuits has blurred the dividing line between the "device" and the "circuit," and thus has made it increasingly important for us to understand deeply the relationship between the internal physics and structure of a device, and its potentialities for circuit performance. Furthermore, the small size and efficient operation of semiconductor devices make possible for the first time a much closer integration between the theoretical and laboratory aspects of the educational process.

To prepare new educational material which would reflect these developments, there was formed in the Fall of 1960 a group known as the Semiconductor Electronics Education Committee (SEEC). This committee is comprised of university and industrial members, brought together by several of the faculty of the Electrical Engineering Department at the Massachusetts Institute of Technology, with Professor C. L. Searle acting as Chairman and Professor R. B. Adler acting as Technical Director. The committee undertook the production of a multipurpose course in semiconductor electronics, designed primarily for use in universities at the third or fourth year undergraduate level.

v

The success of the high-school physics course developed by the Physical Science Study Committee (PSSC) led the SEEC to believe that the same kind of combination used there—text, laboratory experiments, and films, in a complementary format—would be the most practical way of providing uniformly high-quality instruction over the wide range of material involved. It was hoped that this arrangement would lead to broad applicability of the course in the academic world, and also in some professional training activities of industry and government. This book is one in the SEEC series, all volumes of which are listed here:

Vol. 1 (ISP) *Introduction to Semiconductor Physics*, R. B. Adler, A. C. Smith, and R. L. Longini

Vol. 2 (PEM) *Physical Electronics and Circuit Models of Transistors*, P. E. Gray, D. DeWitt, A. R. Boothroyd, and J. F. Gibbons

Vol. 3 (ECP) *Elementary Circuit Properties of Transistors*, C. L. Searle, A. R. Boothroyd, E. J. Angelo, Jr., P. E. Gray, and D. O. Pederson

Vol. 4 (CLT) *Characteristics and Limitations of Transistors*, R. D. Thornton, D. DeWitt, P. E. Gray, and E. R. Chenette

Vol. 5 (MTC) *Multistage Transistor Circuits*, R. D. Thornton, C. L. Searle, D. O. Pederson, R. B. Adler, and E. J. Angelo, Jr.

Vol. 6 (DTC) *Digital Transistor Circuits*, J. N. Harris, P. E. Gray, and C. L. Searle

Vol. 7 (TCM) *Handbook of Basic Transistor Circuits and Measurements*, R. D. Thornton, J. G. Linvill, E. R. Chenette, H. L. Ablin, J. N. Harris, A. R. Boothroyd, J. Willis, and C. L. Searle

These books have all gone through at least one "preliminary edition," many through two or more. The preliminary editions were used in teaching trials at some of the participating colleges and industrial training activities, and the results have been used as a basis for revision.

It is almost impossible to enumerate all those people who have contributed some of their effort to the SEEC. Certain ones, however, have either been active with the Committee steadily since its inception, or have made very major contributions since then. These may be thought of as "charter members," deserving special mention.

From Universities

California, Berkeley: D. O. Pederson
Imperial College London: A. R. Boothroyd△
Iowa State: H. L. Ablin*
M.I.T.: R. B. Adler, P. E. Gray, A. L. McWhorter, C. L. Searle,
     A. C. Smith, R. D. Thornton, J. R. Zacharias, H. J.
     Zimmermann (Research Laboratory of Electronics),
     J. N. Harris (Lincoln Laboratory)
Minnesota: E. R. Chenette
New Mexico: W. W. Grannemann
Polytechnic Institute of Brooklyn: E. J. Angelo, Jr.
Stanford: J. F. Gibbons, J. G. Linvill
U.C.L.A.: J. Willis

From Industries

Bell Telephone Laboratories: J. M. Early, A. N. Holden, V. R.
                       Saari
Fairchild Semiconductor: V. R. Grinich
IBM: D. DeWitt
RCA: J. Hilibrand, E. O. Johnson, J. I. Pankove
Transitron: B. Dale,† H. G. Rudenberg‡
Westinghouse Research Laboratories: A. I. Bennett, H. C. Lin,
                           R. L. Longini§

General management of the SEEC operations is in the hands of Educational Services, Inc. (abbreviated ESI), Watertown, Mass.,

---

△ Now at Queen's University, Belfast.
* Now at the University of Nebraska, Department of Electrical Engineering.
† Now at Sylvania Corp.
‡ Now at A. D. Little, Inc.
§ Now at Carnegie Institute of Technology, Department of Electrical Engineering.

a nonprofit corporation that grew out of the PSSC activities and is presently engaged in a number of educational projects at various levels. In addition to providing general management, ESI has supplied all the facilities necessary for preparing the SEEC films. These are 16-mm sound films, 30 to 40 minutes in length, designed to supplement the subject matter and laboratory experiments presented in the various text books. The film titles are:

"Gap Energy and Recombination Light in Germanium"— J. I. Pankove and R. B. Adler

"Minority Carriers in Semiconductors"—J. R. Haynes and W. Shockley

"Transistor Structure and Technology"—J. M. Early and R. D. Thornton

Pending arrangements for commercial distribution, these films are available (purchase or rental) directly from Educational Services, Inc., 39 Chapel Street, Watertown, Mass.

The committee has also endeavored to develop laboratory materials for use with the books and films. This material is contained in Volumes 1 and 7 of the series.

The preparation of the entire SEEC program, including all the books, was supported at first under a general grant made to the Massachusetts Institute of Technology by the Ford Foundation, for the purpose of aiding in the improvement of engineering education, and subsequently by specific grants made to ESI by the National Science Foundation. This support is gratefully acknowledged.

Campbell L. Searle
Chairman, SEEC
Richard B. Adler
Technical Director, SEEC

Preface

The objectives of this book are twofold: it illustrates the application of transistors in digital circuits in which these devices are used as switches rather than as linear control valves; and it is intended to develop an understanding of the circuit performance and design issues that arise when basic digital circuits are interconnected to form digital information-processing systems. In this regard, the book emphasizes the electronic aspects of digital circuits, and does not deal with the logical design of digital systems.

Although the book stands on its merits as a separate work, it has been developed as one of a series covering transistor electronics from physical background to circuit-design considerations. The series is intended to provide a somewhat complete experience with *one* device of unquestioned technological importance—the transistor. Since this objective normally does not characterize a first course in electronics, we have envisioned the entire series primarily as a "second contact" with electronics. However, by providing several books such as this one, we hope that we have achieved enough flexibility to permit very wide use of the material in whole or in part, from the junior year in the university through the early graduate and professional level.

Readers are assumed to have studied elementary transistor physical electronics and to have a thorough understanding of transistor models and terminal characteristics, both static and dynamic. These matters are considered in two other volumes of the series: *Physical Electronics and Circuit Models of Transistors* (PEM) by P. E. Gray, D. DeWitt, A. R. Boothroyd, and J. F. Gibbons, and *Elementary Circuit Properties of Transistors* (ECP) by C. L. Searle, A. R. Boothroyd, E. J. Angelo, Jr., P. E. Gray, and D. O. Pederson.

This volume has two principal parts. Chapters 2 and 3 deal with simple "building block" circuits—both regenerative and nonregenerative—which use transistors as switching elements. The emphasis here is on the electrical characterization of these basic circuit forms and on the manner in which transistor characteristics affect the behavior of these circuits. On the other hand, Chapters 5 to 7 emphasize the circuit limitations and design considerations that result when basic circuit forms are interconnected to comprise more complex subsystems. The device and circuit characteristics that limit performance of these interconnections are explored, and design considerations are illustrated.

Chapters 1 and 4 are intended to build bridges. Chapter 1 summarizes the aspects of transistor physical electronics, models, and electrical characteristics that are necessary as background for the later chapters of the book. We emphasize that this chapter cannot be considered separately, and is not, in any sense, a substitute for the background material in PEM and ECP. However, it does bring together, with consistency of viewpoint and notation, information that is employed later in the book. Chapter 4 is intended to provide a bridge between the two principal parts of the volume. In this chapter, Boolean notation, Boolean algebra, and the block-diagram realization of Boolean functions are reviewed. Chapters 1 and 4 more accurately contain reference material rather than text material. For this reason it is not advisable to teach all the way through either chapter "in sequence." Instead, these chapters should be referred to at appropriate points in the study of Chapters 2, 3, and 5 to 7.

Chapter 1 contains a rather detailed treatment of the charge-control model for transistor dynamic behavior. This model provides the only satisfactory basis for describing the large-signal transient switching behavior of transistors. However, so many complexities arise when it is applied to multiple-transistor circuits that we have not been able to provide detailed examples of its application in later chapters, and still stay within the scope of the text.

We are indebted to all those members of the SEEC who, by comments and criticisms, have contributed to the publication of this book. We acknowledge the help of Professors R. B. Adler and R. D. Thornton, who made major technical contributions through careful and critical review of the material. Many undergraduate students at M.I.T. have helped significantly in the development of this book by their use of the notes and preliminary editions on which it is based. We are grateful to Mrs. Donna T. Spencer for typing the manuscript and checking the proofs.

J. N. HARRIS
P. E. GRAY
C. L. SEARLE

Cambridge, Massachusetts
September, 1966

Contents

1

Transistors as Switches

1.0 INTRODUCTION

In most systems that process information in digital form, the electrical variables which represent information are nominally two-valued in nature. For example, information may be represented by a voltage or current which ideally takes on one or the other of two discrete values; or the representation may be in terms of a pulse of definite shape which is either present or absent at a specific time. In certain information-processing systems information is represented by the phase of a sinusoidal signal, determined with respect to the phase of a reference signal. Other forms of representation or *scripts* are obviously possible.

Clearly, circuits which are employed in digital systems must respond to signals which are two-valued or binary in nature, and must also produce appropriately quantized output signals. These requirements are in sharp contrast to those which apply to most systems that process information represented by continuous variables, where circuits must respond linearly over large dynamic ranges of the input and output variables.

Of course, variations caused by component and power-supply tolerances as well as by distortion and noise complicate the situation. Specifically, information which is, in principle, represented by discrete voltage levels must, in practice, be represented by ranges or bands of voltage as shown in Fig. 1.1. Similarly, systems in which information is conveyed by the presence or absence at a particular time of a pulse of nominally definite shape must distinguish between spurious signals and pulses which merely deviate from the ideal in shape or arrival time. Usually the main problem presented to the designer of digital circuits is that of insuring that these circuits perform the proper logical function in spite of broad nearly overlapping ranges of values for the nominally two-valued variables. The important consideration is to be able to *distinguish* between the two states. In terms of the voltage-level representation of Fig. 1.1 the emphasis is on the forbidden region between the bands of voltage. The digital circuit designer must insure that under no circumstances will the output of a circuit lie in this forbidden zone (except during transitions from one state to the other) and that the circuit will respond unambiguously to inputs which lie within the permissible ranges on both sides of this forbidden zone.

Transistors are used in digital systems to perform several functions. In some cases a transistor is used to realize a desired logical

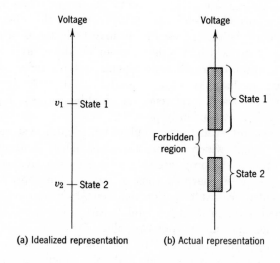

Fig. 1.1 Representation of a binary variable by means of voltage levels.

operation. Frequently transistors are used to provide isolation, to produce power gain, or to restore and standardize the characteristics of a signal. Such circuits possess no memory, in the sense that the value of the output variable depends at any time only on the value of the input variable (or variables) *at that time*. Circuits of this type are referred to as *nonregenerative* switching circuits. Any time delays which do occur in these nonregenerative circuits result only from device limitations.

Other digital circuits which contain transistors may exhibit memory in the sense that the output of the circuit depends intentionally on the past history of the input variable. Such circuits can be used to generate pulses, either continuously or in response to another variable. Circuits of this type usually can be described in terms of a positive feedback mechanism; they are referred to as *regenerative* switching circuits.

The features of the electrical characteristics of transistors which make them useful in switching circuits are essentially the same for both regenerative and nonregenerative circuits. Consequently, we examine the electrical properties of transistor switches in this chapter and defer discussion of specific circuit configurations to Chapters 2 and 3.

Most of the circuits employed in digital systems either use highly nonlinear devices, such as diodes, to set the levels of the variables which represent information, or operate the transistors in a nonlinear manner as the basis for establishing the two ranges of the output variables. In the latter case, it is the emitter and/or collector "diodes" that set the levels. Although it is certainly possible to design transistor circuits which accept and produce two-valued signals while operating as linear amplifiers, this is not usually done in digital systems. Circuits discriminate more accurately between the ranges of values of the input variable, and produce outputs which are less sensitive to the parameters of the transistors and other components, and are thus better quantized, if the circuit operates in a markedly nonlinear manner. Use of such extreme nonlinearity actually amounts to using the ON and OFF *states* of a *pn* junction to represent the binary information, and as such really is a *state representation* rather than a voltage or current level representation.

Digital circuits can be classified on the basis of the transistor operating conditions which correspond to the two states of the circuit. The three classes listed below are used in practical systems.

(1) In one state the transistor is in the *cut-off region* of operation with both junctions reverse biased, while in the other state the transistor operates in the *saturation region* with both junctions forward biased. Such circuits, which are known as *saturating* switching circuits, usually do not employ diodes or other nonlinear elements for level establishment because the transistor itself is operated in such a nonlinear manner.

(2) One state corresponds to operation in the cut-off region, but the other state lies in the *forward active region*, for which the emitter is forward biased and the collector is reverse biased. Such *nonsaturating* circuits often use diodes to establish the output level corresponding to the state in which the transistor is in the active region.

(3) Both states correspond to operation in the forward active region; two markedly different operating points are used. These circuits, which are also *nonsaturating*, usually require diodes for level establishment in *both* states.

As described above, all three systems fundamentally involve state representations; voltage or current levels are permitted to vary, but only to the extent that one band of levels is guaranteed to place a diode or transistor in one state, whereas another band of levels is guaranteed to produce a different state.

We focus attention on saturating circuits and on nonsaturating circuits in which one state corresponds to the cut-off region (types 1 and 2 above) because these classes of circuits are most widely used in digital systems.

The operating condition which lies in the cut-off region is usually referred to as the "OFF" state. In the OFF state the terminal currents, which result from the extraction of thermally generated minority carriers, are very small and essentially independent of the junction voltages. Furthermore, the minority-carrier concentration throughout the base region is negligible compared with its equilibrium value.

The operating state which lies in the forward active region or in the saturation region is called the "ON" state. In both cases the voltage across the forward-biased emitter junction is small and not strongly dependent on the terminal currents. If the transistor is in saturation, the collector-base junction is forward biased, and all terminal-pair voltages are small and weakly dependent on the terminal currents. In both the forward active region and the saturation region the minority-carrier concentration in most of the base is greater than the equilibrium concentration, so that the corresponding store of excess carriers is positive.

A transistor which is constrained by the circuit and input variables to operate in the OFF and ON states described above can be regarded as a switch which is controlled by the *charge* in the base region. This charge appears either as excess mobile charge throughout the neutral base region or as unneutralized impurity charge in the base sides of the junction space-charge layers. Inasmuch as majority carriers enter and leave the base region principally through the base terminal, both the excess charge in the neutral portion of the base and the space-charge-layer charge at the junctions are under the control of the base current. Consequently, a transistor can be switched from one state to the other by supplying or removing base charge at the base terminal.

We begin our analysis of transistor switches and digital circuits by examining the OFF and ON states and the principal features of transitions between states.

1.1 MODELS WHICH DESCRIBE THE TRANSISTOR SWITCH

Our description of the states of a transistor switch is based upon three simple models which describe the electrical behavior of transistors and relate that behavior to the physical mechanisms of transistor action:

(1) The Ebers-Moll model, which relates the terminal currents to the terminal-pair voltages under static conditions.

(2) The charge-control model, which relates the terminal currents to the excess charge in the base under dynamic conditions.

(3) The depletion model of the space-charge layer, which relates the charge in either half of the dipole layer to the junction voltage.

These models are treated in detail elsewhere in the SEEC series. In this section we review these models and summarize the necessary equations.

1.1.1   *The Ebers-Moll Model*

The nonlinear static *V-I* characteristics of a transistor can be approximated by the Ebers-Moll equations, which, for a *pnp* transistor, are:

$$I_E = I_{ES}(e^{qV_{EB}/kT} - 1) \qquad - \alpha_R I_{CS}(e^{qV_{CB}/kT} - 1) \quad (1.1a)$$

$$I_C = -\alpha_F I_{ES}(e^{qV_{EB}/kT} - 1) + I_{CS}(e^{qV_{CB}/kT} - 1) \qquad (1.1b)$$

The coefficients α_F and α_R denote the forward and reverse common-base short-circuit current gains, while I_{ES} and I_{CS} are the short-circuit saturation currents of the junctions. These parameters satisfy the following reciprocity condition:

$$\alpha_F I_{ES} = \alpha_R I_{CS} \qquad (1.1c)$$

An alternative form of Eqs. 1.1*a* and *b* is:

$$I_E = -\alpha_R I_C + I_{EO}(e^{qV_{EB}/kT} - 1) \qquad (1.1d)$$

$$I_C = -\alpha_F I_E + I_{CO}(e^{qV_{CB}/kT} - 1) \qquad (1.1e)$$

The coefficients I_{EO} and I_{CO} denote the open-circuit saturation currents of the junctions:

$$I_{EO} = I_{ES}(1 - \alpha_F \alpha_R) \qquad (1.1f)$$

$$I_{CO} = I_{CS}(1 - \alpha_F \alpha_R) \qquad (1.1g)$$

The corresponding equations for an *npn* transistor differ only in that the currents and voltages change sign. The saturation currents and the short-circuit current gains are defined as positive numbers for both *pnp* and *npn* transistors. The IEEE standard definition of the terminal variables, on which these equations are based, is shown in Fig. 1.2*a*. The equations can be represented by either of the circuit models shown in Fig. 1.2*b* and 1.2*c*.*

Although the Ebers-Moll model is limited in accuracy by several stringent physical assumptions,† it is a useful and important first-order model and provides a reasonable point of departure in the static description of transistor switches.

---

* See, for example, C. L. Searle et al., *Elementary Circuit Properties of Transistors* (hereafter referred to as ECP), Sec. 2.1, John Wiley and Sons, New York, 1964.

† P. E. Gray et al., *Physical Electronics and Circuit Models of Transistors* (hereafter referred to as PEM), Sec. 9.1, John Wiley and Sons, New York, 1964.

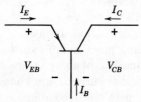

(a) Definition of terminal variables

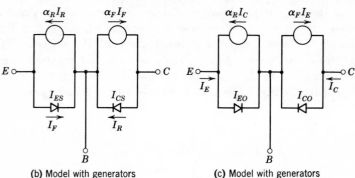

(b) Model with generators
controlled by diode currents

(c) Model with generators
controlled by terminal currents

Fig. 1.2 Models for the nonlinear static behavior of transistors. In parts b and c the diode symbol denotes an idealized *pn* junction diode *V-I* characteristic having the indicated saturation current.

1.1.2 *The Charge-Control Model*

If we neglect the components of terminal current required to change the charge in the space-charge layers, the relationships between the terminal currents of a *pnp* transistor and the forward and reverse components of the excess charge stored in the base region are:

$$i_B = -\left(\frac{q_F}{\tau_{BF}} + \frac{dq_F}{dt}\right) - \left(\frac{q_R}{\tau_{BR}} + \frac{dq_R}{dt}\right) \tag{1.2a}$$

$$i_C = -\frac{q_F}{\tau_F} + q_R\left(\frac{1}{\tau_R} + \frac{1}{\tau_{BR}}\right) + \frac{dq_R}{dt} \tag{1.2b}$$

$$i_E = q_F\left(\frac{1}{\tau_F} + \frac{1}{\tau_{BF}}\right) + \frac{dq_F}{dt} - \frac{q_R}{\tau_R} \tag{1.2c}$$

The charge-control parameters τ_F, τ_{BF}, τ_R, and τ_{BR} are defined as *positive* quantities. Also, positive values of q_F and q_R correspond to *positive* excess-carrier concentrations i.e., q_F and q_R are *positive* when the corresponding junction is *forward biased.*† Consequently the charge-control equations of an *npn* transistor differ only in that the signs of the terminal currents are changed. The parameters τ_{BF} and τ_{BR} characterize the recombination mechanisms in the base for forward and reverse injection respectively. They usually lie in the range from 10 μsec to 10 $n$sec. The parameters τ_F and τ_R relate the forward and reverse components of the excess base charge to the corresponding components of the collector and emitter currents respectively. The charge-control parameters are simply related to the *static* forward and reverse common-emitter short-circuit current gains. Inspection of Eqs. 1.2 shows that

$$\beta_F = \frac{I_C}{I_B}\bigg|_{V_{CB}=0} = \frac{\tau_{BF}}{\tau_F} \qquad (1.3a)$$

$$\beta_R = \frac{I_E}{I_B}\bigg|_{V_{EB}=0} = \frac{\tau_{BR}}{\tau_R} \qquad (1.3b)$$

Consequently τ_F and τ_R are one to two orders of magnitude smaller than τ_{BF} and τ_{BR}. Finally, the two components of the base charge are related to the junction voltages through the Boltzmann relations at the junctions:

$$q_F = \frac{I_{ES}}{1/\tau_F + 1/\tau_{BF}} (e^{qV_{EB}/kT} - 1) \qquad (1.4a)$$

$$q_R = \frac{I_{CS}}{1/\tau_R + 1/\tau_{BR}} (e^{qV_{CB}/kT} - 1) \qquad (1.4b)$$

The charge-control model applies only if the excess charge in the base changes slowly enough so that the change can be regarded as a succession of steady states. This condition is usually met in transistor switches because the useful switching rate is limited by the requirement that the circuit exhibit gain.

† PEM, Sec. 10.1.

1.1.3 *Charge in the Space-Charge Layer*

Charge, in the form of un-neutralized impurity atoms, is stored in the space-charge layer at a *pn* junction. Inasmuch as the magnitude of the charge depends on the junction voltage, changes in junction voltage are accompanied by majority-carrier currents which change the stored charge. The depletion approximation, in which mobile charge in the space-charge layer is neglected in comparison with immobile impurity charge, simplifies analysis of the space-charge layer, and yields reasonably accurate results, except in forward bias.†

Application of the depletion approximation to an *abrupt* junction yields the conclusion that the charge stored in either half of the dipole layer varies as $(\psi_0 - V)^{1/2}$, where ψ_0 is the contact potential of the junction, and V is the voltage applied to the junction. Consequently, the *change from equilibrium* $(V = 0)$ of the charge stored in either half of the dipole layer has the following voltage dependence:

$$q_V \propto [(\psi_0)^{1/2} - (\psi_0 - V)^{1/2}] \qquad (1.5a)$$

The charge change q_V is negative for reverse bias $(V < 0)$ and positive for forward bias $(V > 0)$; it corresponds directly to the majority-carrier charge which must be *added to* either side of the space-charge layer when the voltage changes from zero to V.

In a junction having a *linearly-graded* impurity distribution, the corresponding result is

$$q_V \propto [(\psi_0)^{1/3} - (\psi_0 - V)^{1/3}] \qquad (1.5b)$$

The dependence of q_V on V is illustrated in Fig. 1.3 for both abrupt and graded junctions. Note that the charge change is more important for reverse bias, when the junction voltage can change by tens of volts, than for forward bias, when the junction voltage changes by only a few tenths of a volt.

The charge change q_V can be expressed in terms of the incremental space-charge-layer capacitance C_j. Such a description is frequently more useful than Eqs. 1.5 because the manufacturer usually specifies C_j at a particular reverse voltage, and also de-

† PEM, Sec. 2.3.2.

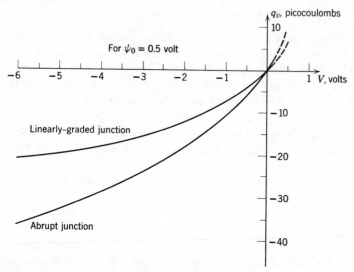

Fig. 1.3. Dependence of charge in the space-charge layer on junction voltage.

scribes its voltage dependence. Since C_j is, by definition, dq_V/dV, q_V can be written:

$$q_V = \int_0^V C_j(u)\ du \qquad (1.6a)$$

where u is the dummy variable of integration. The charge change can be expressed directly in terms of the incremental capacitance at V (see Problem P1.1)

$$q_V = [C_j(V)V]M(V) \qquad (1.6b)$$

The positive dimensionless factor M lies between 1 and 1.5 for a graded junction and between 1 and 2 for an abrupt junction. For large reverse bias ($V \ll -\psi_0$), M approaches its upper limit.

1.2 STATES OF THE TRANSISTOR SWITCH UNDER STATIC CONDITIONS

1.2.1 *The OFF State*

The OFF state of the transistor switch corresponds to operation in the cut-off region with both junctions reverse biased. In this state the terminal currents are, in accordance with Eqs. 1.1:

$$I_E = -I_{ES}(1 - \alpha_F)$$
$$I_C = -I_{CS}(1 - \alpha_R)$$
$$I_B = -(I_E + I_C)$$
$$= I_{ES}(1 - \alpha_F) + I_{CS}(1 - \alpha_R)$$

$$V_{CB} \ll -\frac{kT}{q}$$

$$V_{EB} \ll -\frac{kT}{q}$$

$$(1.7a,b,c)$$

These currents, which are independent of V_{EB} and V_{CB} as long as the voltages are negative and in excess of about 0.1 volt, are commonly in the range of microamperes for germanium devices and in the range of nanoamperes for silicon devices. They are, of course, strongly temperature dependent because they arise from the thermal generation of minority carriers. In most germanium devices the observed temperature dependence is close to the theoretical value of about 10% per degree C, characteristic of bulk minority-carrier generation in the neutral regions near the junctions.* On the other hand, many silicon transistors show a temperature dependence of the OFF currents which is much weaker than would be expected on the basis of the temperature coefficient of 16% per degree C characteristic of bulk minority-carrier generation. This behavior occurs because the observed OFF currents in silicon devices are often dominated by space-charge-layer generation and by surface leakage effects, which are both omitted in the Ebers-Moll model. Figure 1.4 illustrates the temperature dependence of the saturation currents for both germanium and silicon transistors.

The reverse voltages which can be applied to an OFF transistor are limited either by punch-through or by avalanche breakdown.† When punch-through occurs, the incremental resistance between collector and emitter drops to a very low value. In many modern switching transistors, avalanche breakdown occurs before punch-through. As the junction voltage approaches the avalanche-breakdown voltage, the corresponding junction current increases without apparent limit. Although the avalanche breakdown voltage

---

* PEM, Sec. 3.3.4.
† See, for example, R. D. Thornton et al., *Characteristics and Limitations of Transistors* (hereafter referred to as CLT), Sec. 1.6, John Wiley and Sons, New York, 1966.

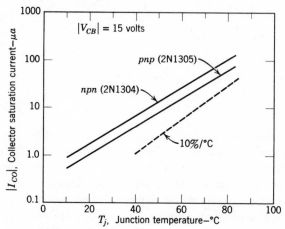

(a) Temperature dependence of the open–circuit collector
saturation current for two germanium alloy transistors

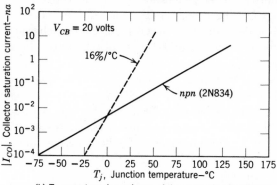

(b) Temperature dependence of the open–circuit collector
saturation current for a silicon diffused transistor

Fig. 1.4. Typical curves of saturation current versus temperature.

of the collector junction is commonly in excess of 100 volts, the
emitter junction may break down at much lower voltages. Emitter
breakdown voltages as low as 3 volts are not uncommon in diffused
transistors. Both breakdown voltages are normally specified by
the manufacturer. If it is relevant, the punch-through voltage is
usually specified as well.

In the OFF state the excess charge stored in the base region is
negligible. However, the charge stored in the space-charge layers

may be quite large. We have seen that this charge can be expressed in terms of the incremental space-charge-layer capacitance C_j and the junction voltage V, in accordance with Eq. 1.6b.

In summary, a transistor switch in the OFF state has negligibly small terminal currents so that the terminal-pair voltages are determined solely by the circuit in which the transistor is embedded. These terminal-pair voltages determine the space-charge-layer charges at the junctions.

1.2.2 *The ON State*

A transistor in the ON state has the emitter junction forward biased. The collector junction may be forward biased as well if the ON state is in the saturation region. The Ebers-Moll equations can be used to express the voltage at a *forward-biased* junction in terms of the terminal currents. For a *pnp* transistor with V_{EB} greater than $5kT/q$ we find from Eq. 1.1d:

$$V_{EB} \cong \frac{kT}{q} \ln\left[\frac{I_E + \alpha_R I_C}{I_{EO}}\right] \cong \frac{kT}{q} \ln\left[\frac{-I_B - (1 - \alpha_R)I_C}{I_{EO}}\right] \quad (1.8a)$$

Also, from Eq. 1.1e, for V_{CB} greater than $5kT/q$:

$$V_{CB} \cong \frac{kT}{q} \ln\left[\frac{I_C + \alpha_F I_E}{I_{CO}}\right] \cong \frac{kT}{q} \ln\left[\frac{-\alpha_F I_B + (1 - \alpha_F)I_C}{I_{CO}}\right]$$
$$(1.8b)$$

For fixed terminal currents, the forward junction voltages vary with temperature in the same manner as the forward voltage of a *pn* junction diode at fixed current.* Specifically, the *magnitudes* of the junction voltages *decrease* with increasing temperature, at a rate of about 1 to 3 mv per °C, for both silicon and germanium devices. Typical data are shown in Fig. 1.5. The curves of Fig. 1.5b also emphasize the fact that the voltage across a forward-biased junction is *not* strongly dependent on the terminal currents, e.g., a change of two orders of magnitude in current has about as much effect as a 30% change in the absolute temperature.

If the ON state lies in the saturation region, the collector-emitter voltage V_{CE} is also of great interest. This voltage which we desig-

---

* See, for example, PEM, Sec. 3.3.4.

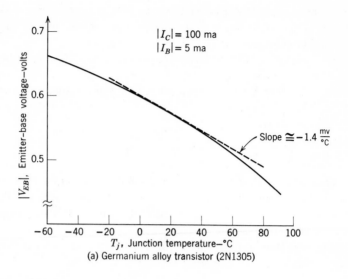

(a) Germanium alloy transistor (2N1305)

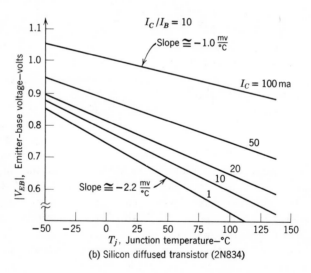

(b) Silicon diffused transistor (2N834)

Fig. 1.5. Temperature dependence of the junction voltages in saturation. Note suppressed zero.

nate $V_{CE}(\text{sat})$ is, from Eqs. 1.8*a* and 1.8*b* for a *pnp* transistor,

$$V_{CE}(\text{sat}) = V_{CB} - V_{EB}$$

$$= \frac{kT}{q} \ln \left[\frac{(1 - \alpha_F)I_{EO}}{I_{CO}} \times \frac{\beta_F I_B/I_C - 1}{I_B/I_C + (1 - \alpha_R)} \right] \quad (1.9a)$$

If we make use of the reciprocity relationship (see Eqs. 1.1*c*, *f*, and *g*)

$$\alpha_F I_{EO} = \alpha_R I_{CO}$$

the value of V_{CE} in the saturated state can be expressed in a form which is more amenable to interpretation:

$$V_{CE}(\text{sat}) = \frac{kT}{q} \ln \left[\alpha_R \frac{\beta_F I_B/I_C - 1}{\beta_F I_B/I_C + (1 - \alpha_R)\beta_F} \right] \quad (1.9b)$$

The transistor is said to be in the *forward-saturation region* when both junctions are forward biased and when current flows *in* at the emitter and *out* at the collector. In this case the collector current is negative ($I_C < 0$), and $V_{CE}(\text{sat})$ is negative. In other words, the emitter junction is more forward biased than the collector junction. The transistor is in the forward saturation region for all currents such that $\beta_F I_B/I_C > 1$.

If, on the other hand, current flows *in* at the collector and *out* at the emitter, a *pnp* transistor in saturation is said to be in the *reverse saturation region*. In this case the collector junction is more forward biased than the emitter so that V_{CE} is positive. In terms of Eq. 1.9*b* this corresponds to positive collector current ($I_C > 0$) and to $-(\beta_R + 1)I_B/I_C > 1$.

The temperature dependence of $V_{CE}(\text{sat})$ can be inferred from Eq. 1.9*b*. In this regard, recall that β_F and α_R are not strongly dependent on temperature. Consequently, for constant terminal currents, the argument of the logarithm in Eq. 1.9*b* is approximately invariant with temperature. Thus $V_{CE}(\text{sat})$ varies linearly with the absolute temperature. Representative data are shown in Figs. 1.6*a* and 1.6*b*.

At medium and large currents, however, one must be cautious about accepting the predictions of the Ebers-Moll model, as summarized by Eq. 1.9*b*. Such effects as the current-dependence

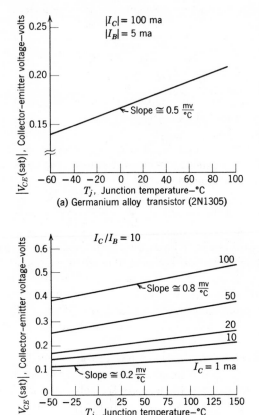

Fig. 1.6. Temperature dependence of $V_{CE}(\text{sat})$. Note suppressed zero.

of β_F and β_R; the voltage drops in the bulk regions of the base, emitter, and collector; and other phenomena associated with high-level injection conditions, may alter substantially the saturation characteristics of a transistor. Accordingly, these characteristics actually depend much more strongly on the detailed physical structure of the transistor than would be predicted by Eq. 1.9b, and this analysis does no more than indicate the way in which the "junction components" of the saturation voltage vary with current and temperature. It also happens that the contribution of bulk voltage drops to the "saturation voltage," tends to increase with temperature (because of the temperature dependence of the carrier mobilities) and decrease with increased current (because of conductivity modulation by the excess carriers). When the saturation characteristics are critically important, as they are in some power-switching and digital circuits, it is usually necessary to rely upon experimental information about the particular transistor type involved, because the foregoing theory based upon the Ebers-Moll model is too greatly oversimplified.

In the ON state the deviations from equilibrium of the space-charge-layer charges are small, as shown in Fig. 1.3, while the excess charge stored in the base region may be quite large. The total excess charge in the ON state is, of course, $q_B = q_F + q_R$. In the forward active region the collector junction is reverse biased. Therefore q_R is negligible and the *total* base charge is smaller, for the same value of I_C, than it would be in the saturation region.

Under static conditions the maximum collector current that can be supported by a fixed base current without leaving the saturation region is determined by:

For forward saturation $\qquad |I_C| \leqslant \beta_F |I_B|$

For reverse saturation $\qquad |I_C| \leqslant (\beta_R + 1)|I_B|$

These equations demonstrate the importance of the short-circuit current gain parameter in switching circuits. Although β_F and β_R are constants in both the Ebers-Moll model and the charge control model, these parameters actually vary significantly with both collector current and temperature.* Typical data for β_F are shown in Fig. 1.7.

In summary, a transistor switch in the ON state has a very small emitter-base voltage. If the ON state lies in the saturation region, the collector junction is also forward biased and all terminal-pair voltages are small and only weakly dependent on the terminal currents. In both cases the terminal currents are determined primarily by the circuit in which the transistor is embedded.

---

* See, for example, CLT, Sec. 1.1.

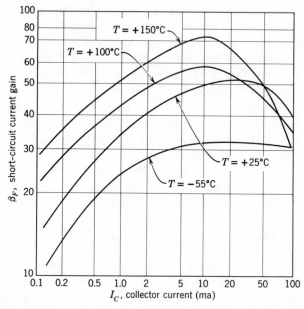

Fig. 1.7. Dependence of the common-emitter short-circuit current gain β_F on temperature and collector current for a silicon transistor.

1.3 TRANSITIONS BETWEEN STATES

Now that we have explored the static characteristics of the ON and OFF states of the transistor switch, and have discussed those states in terms of the charge in the space-charge layers and in the base region, we can consider transitions between states, which cause the charge distributions to change. To be specific we consider a *pnp* transistor; analogous reasoning can be applied to *npn* units.

To turn a transistor switch on we must supply charge to the base region. This charge is required to neutralize the space-charge-layer charges which correspond to the OFF state and to establish enough excess charge in the base region to support whatever collector current is demanded by the circuit when the transistor is on. Conversely, to turn a transistor switch off, we must remove all the excess charge from the base region and must, in addition, remove enough charge from the space-charge layers so that they can support the junction voltages demanded by the circuit with the transistor off. Note that in either turn-off or turn-on, the base charge changes *only as a result of recombination or the flow of base current.*

The basic charge-control equations, Eqs. 1.2, were developed in PEM, Chapter 10 and ECP, Chapter 9. To keep these chapters at as elementary a level as possible, the effects of space-charge-layer charges q_{VE} and q_{VC} were considered only briefly. However, in calculations involving rapid switching of high-speed transistors, q_{VE} and q_{VC} often play a dominant role. Thus it is appropriate at this point to discuss in detail the influence of the space-charge-layer capacitances on switching-circuit performance.

The intrinsic charge-control equations (Eqs. 1.2) can be readily modified to include the effects of q_{VE} and q_{VC}. The appropriate equations* are for a *pnp* transistor

$$i_B = -\frac{q_F}{\tau_{BF}} - \frac{q_R}{\tau_{BR}} - \frac{d}{dt}[q_F + q_R + q_{VE} + q_{VC}] \qquad (1.10a)$$

$$i_C = -\frac{q_F}{\tau_F} + q_R\left[\frac{1}{\tau_R} + \frac{1}{\tau_{BR}}\right] + \frac{d}{dt}[q_R + q_{VC}] \qquad (1.10b)$$

$$i_E = -\frac{q_R}{\tau_R} + q_F\left[\frac{1}{\tau_F} + \frac{1}{\tau_{BF}}\right] + \frac{d}{dt}[q_F + q_{VE}] \qquad (1.10c)$$

The charges q_{VE} and q_{VC} are defined as the charges stored in the emitter and collector space-charge layers relative to the charge stored for zero junction voltage.

In this analysis we use the following conventions.

(1) Positive values of q_F and q_R correspond to positive excess-carrier concentrations (i.e., forward bias). That is, these charge components are defined in terms of the excess-carrier concentrations, and only indirectly in terms of either the minority- or majority-carrier charge store.

(2) Positive values of q_{VE} and q_{VC} accompany forward bias at the corresponding junction.

The internal physical behavior of an *npn* transistor differs from that of a *pnp* unit only in that the roles of holes and electrons are

* PEM, Sec. 10.5 and ECP, Sec. 9.4.

interchanged. Consequently, the charge control equations of an *npn* transistor differ from Eqs. 1.10 only in that *the signs of all three terminal currents are changed*; i.e., each term on the right sides of these equations has the opposite sign for an *npn* unit.

A simple one-transistor switching circuit is shown in Fig. 1.8a. For such a circuit we are usually interested in solving for $i_C(t)$, $v_O(t)$, or various transition times. The base current will, in general, depend on the junction voltages, which depend in a nonlinear fashion on the forward and reverse components of the base charge, which in turn depend on the past history of the base current. While this general situation can be described readily in terms of a set of simultaneous nonlinear differential equations, solutions can usually be obtained only by numerical methods. In order to illustrate some general features of switching circuit transition intervals, we *assume* for the present that the base current is determined solely by the external drive circuit [in this case $v_I(t)$ and R_B]. That is, we assume that the *base drive can be approximated by a current source*. It will turn out that this assumption is frequently justified in practical switching circuits because v_{EB} is small compared with the Thêvenin equivalent source voltage of the circuit which provides the base drive.

Unfortunately, even if we assume a current-source drive so that $i_B(t)$ is known, Eqs. 1.10 remain nonlinear, in the sense that the charges q_{VE} and q_{VC} are nonlinear functions of v_{EB} and v_{CB}, respectively, and these voltages are related to the transistor terminal currents via the external circuit parameters V_{CC}, R_L, etc. For this reason, the complete charge-control equations are rarely used. Instead, simplified equations applicable only over a restricted region of operation are derived. These simplified equations are developed in the following sections.

To make the discussion specific, let us assume that we wish to switch the transistor in Fig. 1.8a from cutoff into saturation, and wish to find equations appropriate for calculating $i_C(t)$ and the transition times. In switching from cutoff to saturation, the transistor clearly will change state several times. To simplify the notation problem, we have defined in Fig. 1.8c and d the pertinent times in terms of the i_C and q_B waveforms. All voltages, currents, and charges will be designated in terms of these times. The detailed

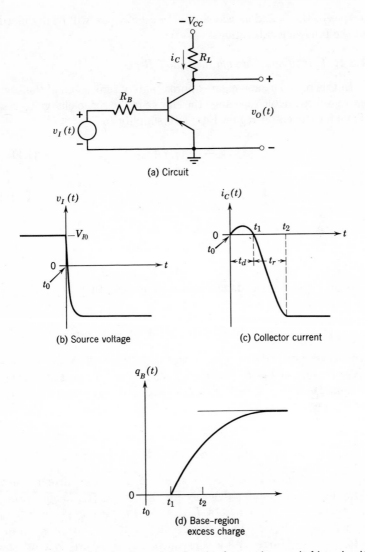

(a) Circuit

(b) Source voltage

(c) Collector current

(d) Base–region
excess charge

Fig. 1.8. Illustrating the dynamics of a simple transistor switching circuit.

shapes of the i_C and q_B waveforms in each region will be discussed in the following subsections.

1.3.1. *Transitions Through the Cutoff Region*

In this region q_F and q_R are approximately zero, so all of the base current is available to change the charge in the space-charge layers. Thus for the cutoff region Eqs. 1.10 simplify to

$$i_B = -\frac{d}{dt}(q_{VE} + q_{VC}) \tag{1.11a}$$

$$i_C = \frac{dq_{VC}}{dt} \tag{1.11b}$$

$$i_E = \frac{dq_{VE}}{dt} \tag{1.11c}$$

If the transistor drive voltage v_I is switched at $t = t_0$ from some known reverse bias voltage V_{I0}, as in Fig. 1.8b, then Eq. 1.11a can be integrated to yield

$$\int_{t_0}^{t_1} i_B(t)\, dt = [q_{VE}(t_0) - q_{VE}(t_1)] + [q_{VC}(t_0) - q_{VC}(t_1)] \tag{1.12}$$

where, as noted above, $q_{VE}(t_0)$ and $q_{VC}(t_0)$ are the space-charge-layer charges at $t = t_0$. Because v_I is assumed constant at a value V_{I0} for t less than t_0, we can find $q_{VE}(t_0)$ and $q_{VC}(t_0)$ from Eqs. 1.5 or 1.6, using

$$V_{EB}(t_0) \cong -V_{I0}$$

$$V_{CB}(t_0) \cong -V_{CC} - V_{I0}$$

We have assumed here that the small positive base current which flows in the OFF state, given by Eq. 1.7c, is small enough to produce negligible drop across R_B. At $t = t_0$, the base current i_B changes to a negative value corresponding to the flow of electrons into the n-type base. As a consequence of this base current, the space-charge layers will discharge.

At the end of the interval in question, the charges are by definition $q_{VE}(t_1)$ and $q_{VC}(t_1)$. If we assume that the circuit is being switched from cutoff into the active region, as in Fig. 1.8, then t_1 defines the instant when the operating point moves from the cutoff region into the active region. This occurs when the emitter junction has several tenths of a volt of forward voltage. For a silicon transistor the junction voltages at this instant will be approximately

$$V_{EB}(t_1) \cong +0.4 \text{ volt}$$

$$V_{CB}(t_1) \cong -V_{CC} + 0.4$$

Note that V_{EB} and V_{CB} change by the same amount between t_0 and t_1. The charges $q_{VE}(t_1)$ and $q_{VC}(t_1)$ can be found from Eqs. 1.6 using these voltages. Assuming we know $i_B(t)$, Eq. 1.12 can now be solved for the time interval $t_1 - t_0$, which is usually called the *delay time* t_d. This is the time interval required for the emitter-base junction to become forward-biased.

The collector current actually *increases* above its OFF-state value during the delay time (see Eq. 1.11b and Fig. 1.8c) because majority carriers must be supplied to the collector half of the space-charge layer. The division of the base current between the collector and emitter is determined by the relative rates of change of q_{VC} and q_{VE}. However, the collector current during this interval is usually negligible compared with the ON-state collector current.

The waveforms of voltage and charge during the interval $t_0 < t < t_1$ are shown in Fig. 1.9 for the special case of a step of base current.

1.3.2 *Transients in the Active Region*

When the emitter junction becomes forward-biased, excess charge begins to accumulate in the base, and substantial collector current will flow. Because the collector diode is reverse-biased, $q_R \cong 0$, so Eqs. 1.10a and 1.10b reduce to

$$i_B = -\frac{q_F}{\tau_{BF}} - \frac{d}{dt}(q_F + q_{VE} + q_{VC}) \qquad (1.13a)$$

$$i_C = -\frac{q_F}{\tau_F} + \frac{dq_{VC}}{dt} \qquad (1.13b)$$

These equations can be further simplified for two frequently encountered situations, as discussed below.

(a) *Final State in the Active Region, Small Load Resistance.* If

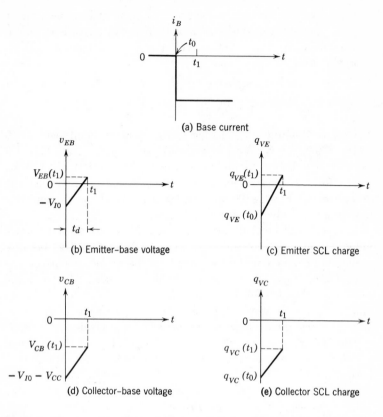

Fig. 1.9. The transition through the cutoff region. The transistor enters the active region at $t = t_1$. For $t_0 < t < t_1$ the base-region excess charge is approximately zero.

the load resistance is small we can assume that the collector current in Eq. 1.13b is dominated by the q_F/τ_F term, and the dq_{VC}/dt term can be neglected because Δv_{CB} will be small. That is,

$$i_C \cong -q_F/\tau_F \qquad (1.14)$$

This approximation is analogous to the small-signal approximation of neglecting the loading of C_μ on the output of the hybrid-π model, while retaining the load of C_μ on the input circuit. Equations 1.13a and 1.14 can now be combined to yield

$$i_B = i_C/\beta_F + \tau_F \frac{di_C}{dt} - \frac{d}{dt}(q_{VE} + q_{VC}) \qquad (1.15)$$

This equation can be used to determine $i_C(t)$ for a specified base drive current once the charges q_{VE} and q_{VC} are expressed in terms of the collector current. The emitter space-charge-layer charge q_{VE} is directly related to i_C through the internal charge-voltage relationship of the transistor. On the other hand, the collector space-charge-layer charge is related to i_C through the parameters of the circuit in which the transistor is embedded. In general, both of these relationships are nonlinear.

(b) *Rapid Traversal of the Active Region.* If the transistor is switched from an initial cutoff condition to a final condition in which the transistor is deep in saturation, then the active region will be traversed so rapidly that almost all of the base current will go into changing the stored charge, and relatively speaking, almost no current will be required to supply recombination. That is, in Eq. 1.13a the base current is dominated by the derivative terms.

At the end of the traversal of the active region, that is, at time t_2, the collector current reaches a saturation value defined by the external circuit parameters.

$$i_C(t_2) \equiv I_C(\text{sat}) \cong -\frac{V_{CC}}{R_L} \qquad (1.16)$$

The time required to traverse the active region can be found by integrating Eq. 1.13a (neglecting q_F/τ_{BF}), and substituting $\tau_F I_C(\text{sat})$ for $-q_F(t_2)$.

$$\int_{t_1}^{t_2} i_B(t)\, dt \cong \tau_F I_C(\text{sat}) + [q_{VE}(t_1) - q_{VE}(t_2)] \\ + [q_{VC}(t_1) - q_{VC}(t_2)] \qquad (1.17)$$

If $i_B(t)$ is known, this equation can be solved for the *rise time* t_r, where t_r is the time interval between the particular instant when the emitter junction becomes forward biased and the instant when the transistor enters saturation. That is,

$$t_r \equiv t_2 - t_1 \qquad (1.18)$$

The complete transition from OFF to ON requires a time

$$t_{on} = t_2 - t_0 = t_d + t_r \qquad (1.19)$$

Waveforms for the various currents and charges during traversal of the active region are shown in Fig. 1.10. These waveforms are again drawn for the simple case of a step of base current.

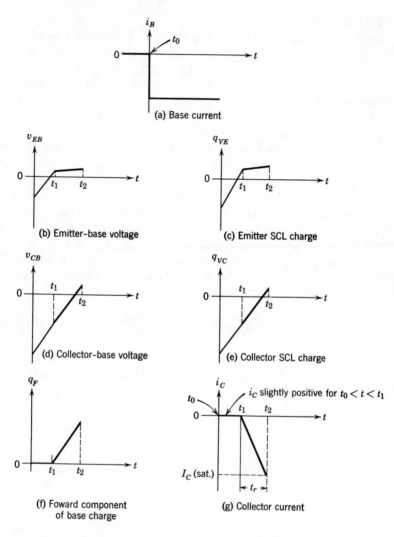

Fig. 1.10. The transition through the active region. The transistor enters the saturation region at $t = t_2$. For $t_0 < t < t_2$ the reverse component of the base-region excess charge is approximately zero.

1.3.3 *Saturation Region*

If the base current is more than adequate to drive the transistor into saturation, as we assumed in Sec. 1.3.2(b) above, then the excess charge in the base $q_B = q_F + q_R$ continues to build up for some time after time t_2 (when the transistor enters saturation). Specifically, q_B builds up until the net rate of recombination is just equal to the final value (steady state) of the base current. In the saturation region both v_{BE} and v_{CB} are nearly constant, so q_{VE} and q_{VC} do not change appreciably. Thus, the behavior of q_F and q_R in this time interval is governed by

$$i_B(t) \cong -\frac{q_F}{\tau_{BF}} - \frac{q_R}{\tau_{BR}} - \frac{d}{dt}(q_F + q_R) \qquad (1.20a)$$

$$I_C(\text{sat}) \cong -\frac{q_F}{\tau_F} + q_R\left(\frac{1}{\tau_R} + \frac{1}{\tau_{BR}}\right) + \frac{dq_R}{dt} \qquad (1.20b)$$

The homogeneous solutions (i.e., the open-circuit natural modes) for $q_F(t)$ and $q_R(t)$ in saturation involve two exponential modes, the time constants of which are widely separated for typical values of β_F and β_R.* Detailed analysis shows that the fast mode represents a redistribution of charge between q_F and q_R, that is, the "slosh" of charge from one part of the base region to the other. On the other hand, the slow mode represents the simultaneous growth or decay of q_F and q_R toward the final values governed by recombination in the base. For most problems the fast-mode time constant is so short that the "slosh" can be assumed to take place instantaneously, and the transistor in saturation can be treated as a single-time-constant system.

If in saturation there is one dominant mode, i.e., the slow mode described above, then it must be possible to approximate Eqs. 1.20 by a pair of equations which have only *one* independent charge variable. We accomplish this simplification by imposing a relationship between q_F and q_R. First, we express $q_F(t)$ as the sum of two charge components:

$$q_F(t) = q_{BO} + q_{FS}(t) \qquad (1.21a)$$

The charge q_{BO}, which is independent of time, is the base charge

* See, for example, PEM, Sec. 10.4.2.

required by a transistor at the *edge* of saturation (no reverse component of base charge). That is,

$$q_{BO} = -\tau_F I_C(\text{sat}) \tag{1.21b}$$

The charge $q_{FS}(t)$ represents the portion of q_F above that required to take the transistor to the edge of saturation.

In terms of these components of q_F, the total excess charge in the base $q_B(t)$ can be written:

$$q_B(t) = q_F(t) + q_R(t)$$
$$= q_{BO} + q_S(t) \tag{1.21c}$$

where

$$q_S = q_{FS}(t) + q_R(t) \tag{1.21d}$$

Clearly $q_S(t)$ denotes the extra base charge in the saturation region. This resolution of q_B into q_{BO} and q_S is illustrated in Fig. 1.11.

When Eq. 1.21a is used to substitute for q_F in the charge-control equation for the collector current (Eq. 1.20b) we obtain:

$$I_C(\text{sat}) = -\frac{q_{BO}}{\tau_F} - \frac{q_{FS}(t)}{\tau_F} + q_R(t)\left(\frac{1}{\tau_R} + \frac{1}{\tau_{BR}}\right) + \frac{dq_R}{dt} \tag{1.22}$$

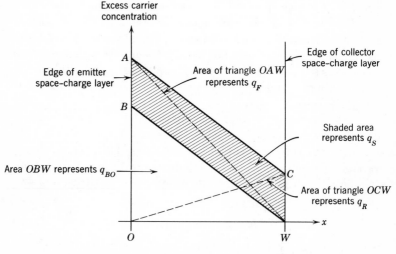

Fig. 1.11. Components of the excess base charge in the saturation region. Although the triangular areas are proportional to the charge components as shown, the constants of proportionality are *not* identical.

or, using the defining equation for q_{BO} (Eq. 1.21b):

$$q_{FS}(t)\left(\frac{1}{\tau_F}\right) = q_R(t)\left(\frac{1}{\tau_R} + \frac{1}{\tau_{BR}}\right) + \frac{dq_R}{dt} \qquad (1.23)$$

We now introduce an approximation which is tantamount to neglecting the fast or "slosh" mode discussed above. *We assume that $q_{FS}(t)$ and $q_R(t)$ are related under dynamic conditions in exactly the same way they are related statically.* Stated in another way, we neglect the dq_R/dt term in Eqs. 1.22 and 1.23. This constraint between $q_{FS}(t)$ and $q_R(t)$ can be used together with the definition of $q_S(t)$ to express the charge-control equation for the base current (Eq. 1.20a) in terms of $q_S(t)$ alone. The result of this algebraic manipulation of the three linear relationships is a *linear* differential equation:

$$i_B(t) = -\frac{q_{BO}}{\tau_{BF}} - \frac{q_S(t)}{\tau_S} - \frac{dq_S(t)}{dt} \qquad (1.24)$$

where τ_S is

$$\tau_S = \frac{\alpha_F(\tau_F + \alpha_R\tau_R)}{1 - \alpha_F\alpha_R} \qquad (1.25a)$$

or, in terms of β_F and β_R

$$\tau_S = \frac{(\beta_R + 1)\tau_F + \beta_R\tau_R}{\beta_F + 1 - \beta_R\beta_F} \qquad (1.25b)$$

It is clear from Eq. 1.24 that the *saturation-region charge-control parameter* τ_S is the apparent lifetime which characterizes the recombination of q_S; it is a weighted average of τ_{BF} and τ_{BR} in which the weighting reflects the composition of q_S from q_{FS} and q_R.

The first term on the right side of Eq. 1.24 can be expressed in terms of $I_C(\text{sat})$. Specifically

$$-\frac{q_{BO}}{\tau_{BF}} = \frac{\tau_F}{\tau_{BF}} I_C(\text{sat}) \qquad (1.26a)$$

or

$$-\frac{q_{BO}}{\tau_{BF}} = \frac{I_C(\text{sat})}{\beta_F} = I_{BO} \qquad (1.26b)$$

This term corresponds to the base current I_{BO} required by a transistor at the edge of saturation. Consequently, an alternate form of the linear saturation-region charge-control equation is

$$i_B(t) - I_{BO} = -\left(\frac{q_S}{\tau_S} + \frac{dq_S}{dt}\right) \tag{1.27}$$

In this form, the charge-control equation emphasizes that the excess of the base current above that required at the edge of saturation is coupled directly to the extra saturation base charge through the usual form of charge conservation relationship.

Either Eq. 1.24 or Eq. 1.27 can be used to determine $q_S(t)$ for a specified base drive. The initial condition for these equations, that is, the condition which applies at the instant of entrance into the saturation region (time t_2 in Fig. 1.8), is clearly

$$q_S(t_2) = 0 \tag{1.28}$$

The general behavior of the charges and terminal variables during the saturation interval (assuming a step base current drive) is shown in Fig. 1.12.

1.3.4 *Transitions from ON to OFF*

In the preceding three sections we have developed the simplified charge-control equations appropriate to each of three regions of transistor operation: cutoff, active, and saturation. In the course of the discussion we have described the complete turn-on transient of a transistor switch. In this section we use these same equations to calculate the behavior of the transistor during turn-off. In the steady ON state the transistor switch has constant base current I_B and constant collector current $I_C(\text{sat})$. The transition to the OFF state is initiated by reducing the base current so that excess carriers are removed from the base, either through the base terminal or by recombination.

The turn-off transition can conveniently be divided into three intervals, as shown in Fig. 1.13.

(1) If the ON state lies in the saturation region there is an interval during which excess carriers are being removed from the base although there is no change in the collector current. This interval ends when $q_R = 0$, at which time the collector junction comes out

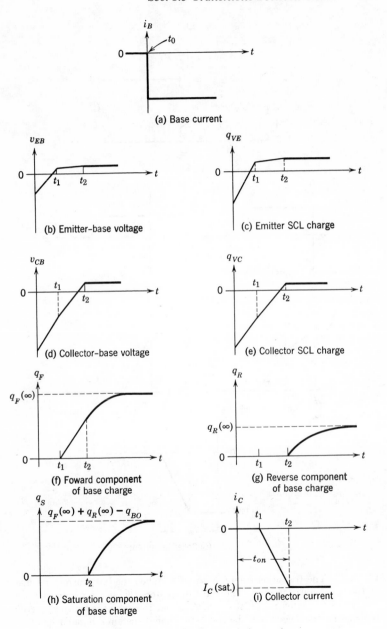

Fig. 1.12. Behavior in the saturation region.

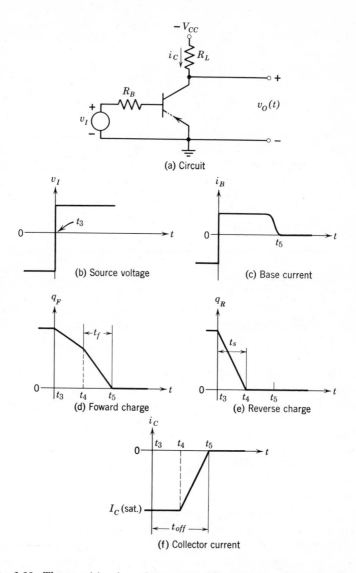

Fig. 1.13. The transition from ON to OFF. When the base current reverses at $t = t_3$, q_S starts to drop. The transistor enters the active region at $t = t_4$ and enters the cutoff region at $t = t_5$. At about this time the emitter junction becomes reverse biased and the transistor cannot sustain a base current.

of forward bias and the transistor leaves the saturation region and enters the forward active region. We designate the duration of this *storage delay interval* as t_s. Changes in the space-charge-layer charges are, of course, negligible during this interval.

(2) The continued removal of excess charge from the base causes i_C to decrease in magnitude as the transistor traverses the active region. The corresponding time interval, which ends when the transistor enters the cut-off region, is called the *fall time* t_f.

(3) The turn-off base current removes majority carriers from the space-charge layers, thereby increasing the magnitudes of the space-charge-layer charges q_{VC} and q_{VE}. This time interval ends when the junction voltages reach the static values that correspond to the OFF state. The turn-off base current cannot, of course, be sustained in the cut-off region. Therefore, the base current must drop to the value given by Eq. 1.7c when the transition is complete.

In evaluating the storage delay time it is certainly possible to work in terms of the forward and reverse components of the base charge, and to find the time required to reduce q_R to zero. However, it is again generally more convenient to work in terms of q_S and τ_S. The storage delay time t_s is obtained by solving Eq. 1.24 for $q_S(t)$, subject to the initial condition that $q_S(0)$ be given by $-(I_B - I_{BO})\tau_S$, and evaluating the time at which $q_S(t) = 0$.

Evaluation of the fall time is entirely analogous to the rise-time analysis of Sec. 1.3.2. If there is turn-off overdrive, i.e., positive base current during the turn-off interval, then frequently we can neglect the recombination component of base current. On this basis the fall time t_f can be found from the expression

$$\int_{t_4}^{t_5} i_B(t)\, dt \cong -\tau_F I_C(\text{sat}) + [q_{VE}(t_4) - q_{VE}(t_5)] \\ + [q_{VC}(t_4) - q_{VC}(t_5)] \quad (1.29)$$

where t_4 is the instant of entry into the active region, and t_5 is the time when the collector current drops to zero.

If the turn-off transition is initiated by simply reducing the base current to zero, as it is in some switching circuits, the excess base charge decays solely by recombination. In this special case the 100% to 10% fall time, which is a more useful description of this turn-off process, is simple $2.3\tau_{BF}$.

The time required for the junction reverse voltages to reach their OFF state static values can be determined by computing the required changes in the space-charge-layer charges, as we did in evaluating the delay time.

Figure 1.13 illustrates the general behavior of the currents, voltages, and charges during the transition from on to off, for the simple case of constant base turn-off current during the transient interval.

1.3.5 *Determination of τ_F and τ_S from Data Sheets*

Manufacturers' data sheets often specify transistor switching parameters in terms of delay time, rise time, storage time, and fall time as a function of collector current, and turn-on and turn-off base current. These measurements are made by supplying a *step* of base current to the transistor under test. Under these special drive conditions, simple expressions can be derived for the above-listed times in terms of the charge-control parameters. Specifically, if the base current is constant at a value I_{B1} during the turn-on interval, then Eqs. 1.12 and 1.17 can be solved to yield

$$t_d \cong \frac{[q_{VE}(t_0) - q_{VE}(t_1)] + [q_{VC}(t_0) - q_{VC}(t_1)]}{I_{B1}} \tag{1.30}$$

$$t_r \cong \frac{\tau_F I_C(\text{sat}) + [q_{VE}(t_1) - q_{VE}(t_2)] + [q_{VC}(t_1) - q_{VC}(t_2)]}{I_{B1}} \tag{1.31}$$

where we assume $\beta_F |I_{B1}| \gg |I_C(\text{sat})|$

If we assume a turn-on base current I_{B1} and a step of turn-off base current I_{B2}, then the storage time becomes, from Eq. 1.24,

$$t_s \cong \tau_S \ln \left[\frac{I_{B2} - I_{B1}}{I_{B2} - I_C(\text{sat})/\beta_F} \right] \tag{1.32a}$$

If the turn-off base current is large enough, then we can extrapolate the initial slope of the exponential in $q_S(t)$, and find for the storage time:

$$t_s \cong \tau_S \left(\frac{I_{B1} - I_C(\text{sat})/\beta_F}{I_{B1} - I_{B2}} \right) \tag{1.32b}$$

The fall time for large turn-off base current, based on Eq. 1.29, is

$$t_f = \frac{-\tau_F I_C(\text{sat}) + [q_{VE}(t_4) - q_{VE}(t_5)] + [q_{VC}(t_4) - q_{VC}(t_5)]}{I_{B2}} \tag{1.33}$$

This expression would indicate that fall time is independent of the turn-on base current I_{B1}. However, measured characteristics show some dependence. This probably arises from charge stored in remote regions of the base (see PEM, Sec. 10.6).

The above expressions, combined with Eq. 1.6 for evaluating q_{VE} and q_{VC}, can be used to find τ_F and τ_S from manufacturers' data sheets. It is important to note, however, that these equations *cannot* be used in general for the calculation of switching times in switching circuits. Specifically, they *do not apply to the common practical problem in which the transistor under consideration is being driven by another transistor*, because in this case the base drive will not in general be a step. This matter is discussed further in Sec. 2.1.2.

PROBLEMS

P1.1 The charge q_V associated with the space-charge layer at a *pn* junction can be defined in terms of the incremental space-charge capacitance, as in Eq. 1.6a.

(a) Show that q_V can also be expressed in the form given in Eq. 1.6b, and express $M(V)$ as a definite integral. *Suggestion:* Note that $C_j(u)$ can be written

$$C_j(u) = C_j(V)f(u, V)$$

where $f(u, V)$ depends on the impurity distribution at the junction.

(b) For an abrupt junction, the incremental capacitance has the following voltage dependence

$$C_j(V) = \frac{K}{(\psi_0 - V)^{1/2}}$$

where K is a constant and ψ_0 is the contact potential. Evaluate $M(V)$ for an abrupt junction. Sketch and dimension $M(V)$ vs. V for $-100\psi_0 < V < \psi_0/2$.

P1.2 An alloy transistor can be characterized as having abrupt junctions. Consider a device of this type which has an incremental collector space-charge capacitance of 5 pf at a collector-base voltage of 20 volts (reverse bias). How much charge must be removed from the collector space-charge layer when the collector-base voltage changes from a forward bias of 0.3 volts to a reverse bias of 30 volts. Assume $\psi_0 = 0.6$ volt.

P1.3 The collector-to-emitter voltage of a saturated transistor is given by Eq. 1.9b.

(a) Use this expression to evaluate the value of $V_{CE}(\text{sat})$ that obtains when the transistor is driven heavily into forward saturation, i.e., when $\beta_F |I_B| \gg |I_C|$. Note that this voltage is a lower bound for $V_{CE}(\text{sat})$ for forward saturation. Since it corresponds to the collector-to-emitter voltage with negligible collector current (but large base drive) it is sometimes called the *offset voltage* of a transistor switch.

(b) Assuming that α_F is greater than α_R, show that the offset voltage will be smaller if the collector and emitter terminals of the device are reversed.

P1.4 This problem is based on the circuit of Fig. 1.8a with the following parameters

$$V_{CC} = 10 \text{ volts}$$

$$R_L = 1 \text{ k}$$

$$R_B = 10 \text{ k}$$

The *pnp* transistor, which is assumed to have *abrupt* junctions, has the following parameters:

Junction contact potential: $\psi_0 = 0.5$ volt

Incremental emitter junction capacitance:
$$C_{je} = 5 \text{ pf at } V_{EB} = -10 \text{ volts}$$

Incremental collector junction capacitance:
$$C_{jc} = 10 \text{ pf at } V_{CB} = -10 \text{ volts}$$

Forward charge-control parameter: $\tau_F = 2$ nsec

Reverse charge-control parameter: $\tau_R = 15$ nsec

Forward common-emitter current gain: $\beta_F = 50$

Reverse common-emitter current gain: $\beta_R = 10$

At $t = 0$ the drive voltage v_I changes abruptly from $+2$ volts to -10 volts.

(a) Estimate the *delay time* t_d, which is the time required for the emitter-base junction to change from 2 volts of reverse bias to the threshold of forward conduction. Assume that the delay time interval ends when $v_{EB} = 0.2$ volt. *Make reasonable approximations.*

(b) Estimate the *rise time* t_r, which is the time required for $|i_C|$ to increase from approximately zero at the end of the delay time interval to V_{CC}/R_L, which is its approximate value with the transistor in saturation. Assume that the rise time is small enough so that the recombination component of the base current can be neglected.

(c) Use your result in (b) to estimate the base charge absorbed by recombination during the rise time interval. Is the approximation of rapid traversal of the active region which was made in (b) reasonable?

(d) Compute the static excess charge in the neutral base region when the transistor is saturated.

P1.5 The dynamic behavior of q_F and q_R in the saturation region of operation is governed by Eqs. 1.20. This problem is concerned with the natural frequencies of the system that exist when the base and collector currents are *fixed* (the "open-circuit" natural frequencies). For simplicity in the analysis assume

$$\left.\begin{array}{l} \tau_{BF} = \tau_{BR} = \tau_B \\[4pt] \tau_F = \tau_R = \tau \end{array}\right\} \; \tau_B/\tau = \beta$$

(a) Determine the natural frequencies which appear in the homogeneous portions of the solutions for q_F and q_R. Show that these natural frequencies are widely separated.

(b) What is the characteristic mode associated with the lower natural frequency? That is, how are the components of q_F and q_R that exhibit this frequency related?

(c) What is the characteristic mode associated with the higher natural frequency?

P1.6 Verify Eqs. 1.24 and 1.25. Demonstrate that the constraint which is applied to q_F and q_R in developing Eq. 1.24 is negligibly different from the constraint which results if we assume that q_F and q_R exhibit *only* the lower natural frequency found in Problem P1.5.

P1.7 This problem is based on the circuit of Fig. 1.8a, and uses the parameters given in Problem P1.4. It is concerned with the transition from ON to OFF, which is initiated at $t = 0$ by an abrupt change of v_I from -10 volts to $+2$ volts.

(a) Determine the *storage delay time* t_s required for the base-region excess charge to decrease to a value just sufficient to bring the transistor to the edge of the active region.

(b) Determine the *fall time* t_f during which the transistor traverses the active region. The fall time ends when $i_C \cong 0$ and when v_{EB} has a value corresponding to the threshold of conduction. Assume that recombination is negligible during the fall time interval and comment on the validity of this assumption.

(c) Estimate the time required for the system to reach equilibrium in the OFF state. That is, determine the interval between the time the transistor leaves the forward active region and the time at which static conditions are reached. Make reasonable approximations.

Nonregenerative Switching Circuits

2.0 NONREGENERATIVE CIRCUIT FUNCTIONS

Transistors are used in nonregenerative switching circuits to perform the following functions:

(1) Realization of a logical operation.

(2) Signal standardization.

(3) Power gain.

(4) Isolation.

An example of a transistor circuit which performs a logical operation, that of *complementation*, is shown in Fig. 2.1*a*. This circuit is a simple common-emitter amplifier which is biased to have the static transfer characteristic shown in Fig. 2.1*b*. It is clear from this transfer characteristic that the circuit will produce one or the other of two output values, which are essentially independent of the characteristics of the transistor, if the input is constrained to take one or the other of two widely separated ranges of values. More precisely, if v_A is less than about 1.1 volts the transistor is cut off and v_B is approximately 10 volts (the collector supply voltage). If, on the other hand, v_A is greater than about 6.5 volts the transistor is saturated and v_B is approximately zero. These relationships are summarized in Table 2.1.

TABLE 2.1

Voltage relationships

V_A (volts)	V_B (volts)
< 1.1	~ 10
> 6.5	~ 0

In a digital system the voltages v_A and v_B correspond to *binary variables* **a** and **b**. The relationship between the values of the binary

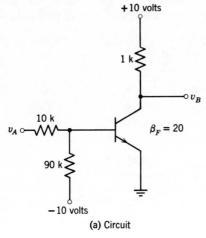

(a) Circuit

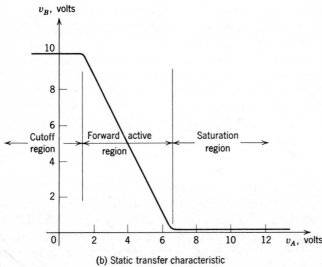

(b) Static transfer characteristic

Fig. 2.1. A transistor inverter which performs the logical operation of complementation. Voltages are specified with respect to ground.

variable and the ranges of the physical variable is an arbitrary one.
For the purpose of this discussion we make the following assignment:

Range of voltage	Value of binary variable
0 to +1 volt	0
+7.0 to +10 volts	1

The logical relationship between the binary variables which is produced by the overdriven amplifier is shown in Table 2.2. This relationship is that of *complementation*. The variable **b** is the *complement* of **a**.

TABLE 2.2
Table of combinations

a	b
0	1
1	0

Although the principal function of the "inverter" circuit shown in Fig. 2.1 is the performance of the specified logical operation of complementation, the circuit has other useful properties. Specifically, the output variable is better quantized or standardized than the input variable. Any input voltage ranging from several volts negative* to about 1.1 volts positive produces an output voltage which is very nearly equal to 10 volts because the transistor is cut off. Similarly, any input voltage ranging from about 6.5 volts up to a value set by the power dissipation limit in the input resistor causes the transistor to be saturated and yields an output voltage of very nearly zero volts.

The inverter circuit provides power gain as well. When **a** has the value **1**, the circuit can be characterized by an input resistance of about 10 k. Furthermore, when the output variable **b** is **1** the output resistance is 1 k. Consequently the inverter can be loaded by as many as three other circuits like it (having an input resistance of 10 k) before the variable v_B corresponding to the output drops below the prescribed lower limit of its range, which is 7 volts. Thus the inverter possesses gain, which is frequently described as *logical gain*. Because it is capable of driving three other circuits having the same input requirements as itself, the circuit is said to have a *fan-out* ratio of 3 (see Sec. 4.3.6).

---

* The lower limit on v_A is set by avalanche breakdown of the *emitter* junction.

Finally, the inverter circuit provides isolation in the sense that the input variable v_A is substantially unaffected by the circuit which is driven by the output variable v_B.

A second example of the use of a transistor in a nonregenerative switching circuit is shown in Fig. 2.2. The parameter values are chosen so that the transistor is saturated if one or more of the input variables has a voltage which corresponds to the **1** value of the associated binary variable.* Consequently the output binary variable **d** is **1** if and only if neither **a** nor **b** nor **c** is **1**. For this reason the circuit is described as a *NOR* gate. We investigate the logical uses of such gates in Sec. 4.3.5.

Although the transistor in this circuit is essentially an inverter and thus performs a certain logical function, its principal role is that of signal standardization. Note that the base current of the transistor varies over a range of nearly three to one depending upon whether one, two, or three of the input variables is in the **1** state. However, the transistor is saturated for all such conditions, so that under these conditions the output voltage v_D is essentially independent of the base current.

---

* We assume that the correspondence between voltage and the associated binary variable is the same as that discussed in connection with Fig. 2.1. That is, the more positive voltage corresponds to the "1" value of the binary variable.

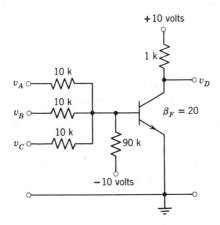

Fig. 2.2. Transistor-resistor logic circuit.

In both of the examples used in this section the ON state of the transistor is in the saturation region. *Saturating circuits* of this type are considered in more detail in Sec. 2.1. Another class of switching circuits, called *nonsaturating circuits*, in which the ON state lies in the forward active region, is examined in Sec. 2.2.

2.1 SATURATING CIRCUITS

The heart of most saturating switching circuits is the overdriven common-emitter amplifier shown in Fig. 2.1. This circuit may be used simply as an inverter, to provide complementation of a binary variable or to standardize a signal, or it may be employed with other components to produce more complex logical functions.

2.1.1 *Static Conditions*

The output voltage of a saturating transistor switch will be reasonably well quantized only if the transistor is driven between cutoff and saturation. The circuit parameters, the input signal amplitude ranges, and the load which is driven by the circuit must be chosen so that under static conditions the ON state lies in the saturation region with both junctions forward biased and the OFF state lies in the cut-off region with both junctions reverse biased.

Saturation of the transistor occurs if the base current is large enough to support recombination of the excess base charge required by the ON-state collector current, which is, of course, determined by the circuit and not by the transistor. If the magnitude of the static ON-state collector current is denoted by $|I_C(\text{sat})|$, the excess base charge required to take the transistor to the edge of saturation ($V_{CB} = 0$) is simply $\tau_F|I_C(\text{sat})|$, where τ_F is the forward charge-control parameter. The associated base current magnitude is

$$|I_B| = \frac{\tau_F|I_C(\text{sat})|}{\tau_{BF}} = \frac{|I_C(\text{sat})|}{\beta_F} \tag{2.1}$$

where τ_{BF} is the effective base-region lifetime for forward injection and β_F is the forward common-emitter short-circuit current gain.

The base current given by Eq. 2.1 is the *minimum* current that will ensure saturation of the transistor. Invariably, the base current is larger than this minimum so that the transistor has more excess base charge than is necessary to support the circuit-defined collector current. This extra base charge appears as a reverse component and is associated with forward bias at the collector junction.

There are several reasons why the static base current must be larger than the minimum value given by Eq. 2.1. First, transistors of a particular type exhibit a range of values for β_F which may be quite broad. Many transistor types show 2 to 1 ranges of variation in β_F at a particular operating point, and 10 to 1 variations are not uncommon. Clearly a circuit which is to operate properly with *any* transistor of a certain type number must be designed so that adequate base current is provided for the units which have the *minimum* specified value of β_F. Consequently, units which have larger values of β_F will have more than enough base drive.

Second, the collector current in the ON state depends on the load with which the circuit operates, and this load generally is not constant. Inasmuch as Eq. 2.1 must be satisfied for the largest possible value of $|I_C(\text{sat})|$, the base current will be more than adequate for those operating conditions in which the collector current is less than maximum.

Third, normal variations of component values and power supply voltages cause variations in the base drive and in the load current. The circuit design must insure that the base current is adequate for operation in the saturation region even with the most unfavorable combination of component and power supply values. Therefore, the base current will be more than adequate under most conditions.

One of the processes by which the circuit designer insures that the circuit will be in the proper state in spite of transistor variations from unit to unit, load and drive variations, and component and power supply tolerances is called *worst-case design*. It involves determining the worst possible combination of circuit and device parameters, under the most unfavorable environmental conditions, and specifying the circuit so that it functions properly even in this worst-possible case. Such a design philosophy is extremely conservative, inasmuch as the worst case may be an exceedingly improbable event. Nevertheless, worst-case design guarantees proper circuit performance under all conditions short of component failure (see Problems P2.2 through P2.4).

The OFF state of a transistor switch corresponds to operation in the cut-off region with both junctions reverse biased. In all switching circuits the collector junction becomes reverse biased when the base drive is reduced. Consequently, we may focus attention on the emitter junction in our investigation of circuit conditions in the OFF state.

Some switching circuits, such as those shown in Figs. 2.1 and 2.2, include a bias arrangement which insures that the emitter junction is reverse biased when the input signals are such that the transistor should be OFF. The magnitude of the reverse voltage at the emitter junction is not critical, a reverse voltage of about 0.1 volts results in the maximum possible reduction in collector current, so that greater reverse voltages have no significant effect on the OFF-state collector current. There is no advantage in a circuit design which produces large emitter-junction reverse voltages in the OFF state. In fact, excessive reverse voltages increase the charge in the emitter space-charge layer, thereby increasing the delay time unnecessarily (see Sec. 1.3.1).

The saturation currents I_{ES} and I_{CS} are so small in most modern transistors that the collector current of a switch in the OFF state is substantially independent of the emitter junction voltage for junction voltages less than several tenths of a volt in the forward direction. This is illustrated in Fig. 2.3, which shows I_C vs. V_{BE}

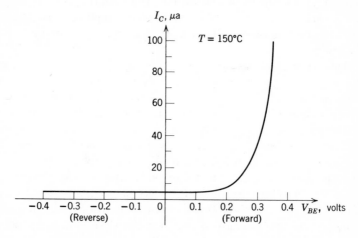

Fig. 2.3. Dependence of collector current on base-emitter voltage in an *npn* silicon transistor at 150°C.

for a silicon switching transistor. A switching circuit which uses this transistor and which has an ON-state collector current of several milliamperes is effectively in the OFF state if the emitter-base voltage is less than about 0.3 volts. Below this voltage, which is referred to as the *base-emitter threshold voltage* V_{BET}, the injection of minority carriers into the base by the emitter junction has an insignificant effect on the collector current. Threshold voltages are smaller in germanium transistors because the saturation currents are larger. Usually threshold voltages for germanium lie in the range from 0.1 to 0.2 volts at room temperature. The threshold voltage reflects the exponential temperature dependence of the saturation currents, and thus has a temperature coefficient of -2 to -3 millivolts per degree C.

The fact that a transistor is essentially cut off for small forward voltages at the emitter is reflected in the design of switching circuits. For example, the second transistor in the direct-coupled gate shown in Fig. 2.4 contains no provision for reverse biasing the emitter in the OFF state, but operates with a small forward emitter-base voltage approximately equal to the saturated collector-emitter voltage of the first transistor. This voltage, which is the *difference* between the forward voltages on the two junctions of the first transistor, is less than the threshold voltage of the second transistor. Consequently, the second transistor is OFF when all of the transistors which drive it are ON.

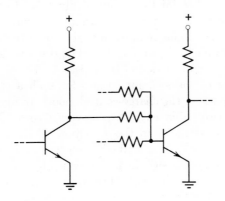

Fig. 2.4. Direct-coupled transistor logic gate.

In practice, direct-coupled circuits using silicon transistors operate on this basis satisfactorily. However, in germanium because the threshold voltages are so much smaller, other effects such as collector body resistance come into play, and direct-coupled logic will work with germanium only if the transistors are carefully selected to have a low V_{CE}(sat).

In the design of a transistor switching circuit, the static OFF state must be examined under worst-case conditions to insure satisfactory operation (see Problems P2.2 through P2.4). This usually implies consideration of the highest environmental temperature, for which the saturation currents are at their maximum values.

2.1.2 *Transient Response*

The principal feature of the transient response of saturating transistor switching circuits is storage delay time. As discussed in the preceding section, the ON-state static base current is invariably greater than the minimum value required to saturate the transistor. Frequently the ON-state base current is several times larger than the minimum value. Consequently, there is extra charge stored in the base region in the ON state, and this charge must be removed, either by recombination or by a turn-off base drive, before the collector junction can become reverse biased so that the collector current can decrease in magnitude. A typical transient response is shown in Fig. 2.5*b* for the circuit of Fig. 2.5*a*. In this case, for which the static ON state base current is considerably larger than the minimum value required for saturation, the storage delay time is comparable to the sum of the delay, rise, and fall times, and causes appreciable distortion of the pulse.

Calculations of the switching times for such a circuit can be made on the basis of the charge-control model. In most saturating circuits the base drive current is governed principally by the external base resistance and the amplitude of the input voltage, and is dependent only to second order on the emitter-base voltage of the transistor being switched. Consequently, such circuits can be regarded as current-driven, and the transient analysis of Sec. 1.3 can be applied directly.

The storage delay time can be reduced by providing a reverse base current which removes excess carriers from the base, thus

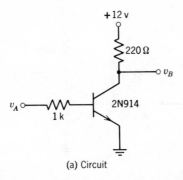

(a) Circuit

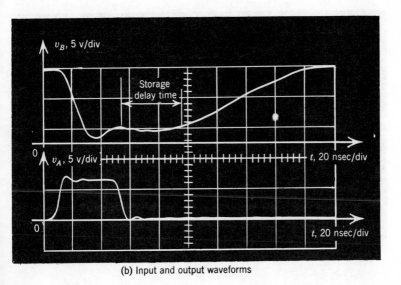

(b) Input and output waveforms

Fig. 2.5. Storage delay time in a saturating switching circuit.

augmenting the rate of decay of the store of excess carriers. Such a
transient component of base current can be provided by bridging
the base resistor with a *speed-up capacitor* as shown in Fig. 2.6.
In the ON state, the voltage across the capacitor is $I_B|R$ so that
the capacitor accumulates a charge of $|I_B|RC$. If C is adjusted so
that the charge on the capacitor is equal to or greater than the
total excess charge in the base in the ON state, the impulse-like

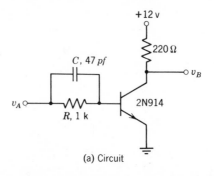

(a) Circuit

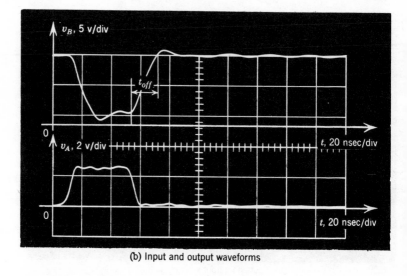

(b) Input and output waveforms

Fig. 2.6. Reduction of storage delay time by means of a speed-up capacitor. Note that the total turn-off time, t_{off}, is much less than without the speed-up capacitor.

current, which results from the discharge of C when the input voltage drops, removes the excess base charge very rapidly, thereby reducing both the storage delay time and the fall time.

The speed-up capacitor also provides an impulse-like turn-on current when the transistor is switched on, thereby reducing the delay time and the rise time.

The waveforms of Fig. 2.6 and the accompanying discussion are based on the tacit assumptions that the input pulse has rise and fall times that are negligibly small compared with the response times of the transistor, and that the pulse source can supply the peak current associated with the impulse-like components of the base drive. Neither of these conditions is satisfied in most practical switching circuits. The drive pulses have rise and fall times which are comparable to the response time of the transistor being driven, and peak drive currents are limited by the circuit. We illustrate the consequences of these limitations in terms of the simple direct-coupled circuit shown in Fig. 2.7a. We assume that initially the first transistor is off so that the second transistor is on and is overdriven by the static base current provided by V_C through R_1 and R_3. We further *assume* that the first transistor is driven in such a way that excess charge accumulates in its base at a constant rate during the time that this transistor is switching from off to on. We denote the corresponding rate of increase of the forward component of the collector current by a.

An approximate circuit model, which is valid *until the first transistor saturates*, is shown in Fig. 2.7b. This circuit neglects the base-emitter voltage of the second transistor in comparison with v_1, the collector voltage of the first transistor, and assumes that the first transistor saturates *before* the second transistor cuts off.

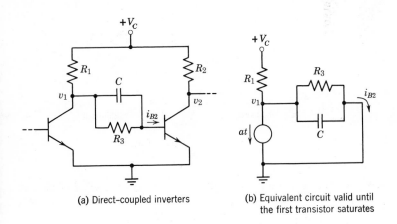

(a) Direct–coupled inverters

(b) Equivalent circuit valid until the first transistor saturates

Fig. 2.7. Circuits used in the analysis of transient response.

When the first transistor saturates, the base current i_{B2} drops abruptly to zero.

We wish to determine the effect of the capacitor C on the base current i_{B2} and on the collector-to-ground voltage v_1 of the first stage. This requires solution of a single-time-constant RC network which is driven by a constant voltage source together with a ramp current source, as shown in Fig. 2.7b.

Analysis of the circuit model yields the transient waveforms shown in Fig. 2.8a and b. The waveforms which result if the capacitor is omitted are shown dotted. It is evident from these curves that the time required for the first transistor to switch from off to on is increased by the speed-up capacitor. However, the time required for the second transistor to turn off may be substantially reduced, because the speed-up capacitor removes excess charge from the base which would otherwise have to recombine before the second transistor could come out of saturation. The excess charge thus removed is proportional to the shaded area in Fig. 2.8b. If this charge were not removed by the reverse base current associated with C, it would have to disappear from the base by recombination, thus increasing the storage delay time of the second transistor. Of

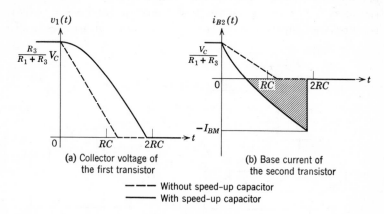

(a) Collector voltage of
the first transistor

(b) Base current of
the second transistor

– – – – Without speed-up capacitor
———— With speed-up capacitor

Fig. 2.8. Transients which occur when the first transistor switches from off to on. R denotes the equivalent parallel resistance: $R_1 \| R_3$. The rate of change of the collector current of the first transistor for which these curves apply is $a = (\frac{4}{5})(1/RC)(V_C/R_1)$.

course, the turn-off base drive produced in this circuit by C does not remove the stored charge as rapidly as the impulse-like component of reverse base current associated with the voltage-driven circuit of Fig. 2.6. The relative turn-off times for these two cases could be found by using Eq. 1.29.

The first transistor must be capable of supplying a collector current of $I_{BM} + V_C/R_1$, where I_{BM} is the peak amplitude of the reverse base current shown in Fig. 2.8b. Although the peak current requirement presents no problem in our illustrative example, it must be considered in a practical circuit.

An equivalent circuit similar to that shown in Fig. 2.7b can be used to investigate the effect of the speed-up capacitor when the first transistor switches off. The capacitor causes the excess base charge in the second transistor to increase more rapidly than it would without a capacitor, thereby reducing both the delay time and the rise time. In many cases the first transistor cuts off before its collector voltage reaches its static value. In such cases the base current is governed by a simple RC decay.

When speed-up capacitors are used in a saturating switch, there is a trade-off between logical gain and switching speed. Specifically, faster switching can be accomplished only by driving the transistor with larger peak currents, thereby changing the internal charge stores more rapidly. Therefore, fewer circuits can be driven by the output of a single gate.

2.1.3 *Clamped Circuits*

One limitation of the switching circuits that have been considered thus far is the dependence of the collector voltage in the OFF state on the load which is driven by the circuit. Since the collector-emitter terminals of the transistor look like an open circuit in the OFF state, the static collector voltage is, in effect, set by a voltage divider comprised of the collector resistor and the equivalent load resistance, and thus changes as the load changes. This variation can be eliminated by adding a power supply and a diode as shown in Fig. 2.9. The diode "catches" the collector voltage at approximately V_D volts and does not allow it to rise to the full collector supply voltage.

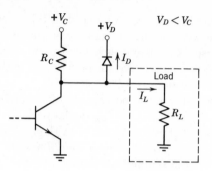

Fig. 2.9. Clamp diode which stabilizes the OFF state collector voltage.

The diode current with no external load is

$$I_D = \frac{V_C - V_D - V_F}{R_C} \tag{2.2}$$

where V_F denotes the diode forward drop. Consequently the load current can vary from zero to a maximum value given by Eq. 2.2 before the diode opens and the collector-emitter voltage begins to drop.

The clamp diode causes the OFF-state output voltage to be less sensitive to collector power supply voltage changes and to resistor variations. In addition, it reduces the incremental output resistance when the circuit is in the OFF state. Consequently, the output is less susceptible to noise when a clamp diode is used. The clamp diode also reduces the time required for the output voltage to change from one state to the other. It limits the voltage waveform to the initial portion of an exponential, the asymptote of which lies outside the range of output voltages. These beneficial effects are obtained at the price of increased power dissipation and somewhat greater circuit complexity.

2.1.4 *Circuits for Use with Capacitive Loads*

The overdriven common-emitter amplifier is unsatisfactory for driving loads which have a large shunt capacitance, such as may be contributed by cables or extensive wiring. The difficulty arises because of the asymmetric nature of the output provided by the overdriven amplifier; in switching on the amplifier can provide output currents which are far in excess of the static current in the collector resistor, while in switching off the load current can never exceed the current in the collector resistor, because the collector current of the transistor cannot reverse direction.

We employ the circuit of Fig. 2.10a to illustrate the transient response of an overdriven amplifier operated with a capacitive load. We assume for simplicity that the transistor collector current responds to the base drive in times that are negligibly small compared with the response time of the output voltage.* The transistor is driven by a step of base current of amplitude I_B as shown in Fig. 2.10b. Consequently the collector current is initially

$$i_C = \beta_F I_B \qquad (2.3)$$

This value of collector current persists until the transistor saturates, when it drops abruptly to the static value of V_C/R_C. The resulting collector voltage waveform is shown in Fig. 2.10c. As the waveforms are drawn, the base current amplitude is about three times as large as the current required to just saturate the transistor, so the collector voltage falls to zero in about one-half a time constant.

When the base current reverses polarity, the collector current drops to zero almost immediately. Therefore, v_{CE} charges toward the collector supply voltages exponentially and the rise time is about six times as long as the fall time.

Several circuit modifications can be employed to reduce the time required for the capacitor to charge when the transistor switch turns off. For example an emitter follower can be used, as shown in Fig. 2.11a. If the rate of change of the capacitor current is small enough so that the dynamics of the emitter-follower transistor are unimportant, the current gain of the emitter follower reduces the time constant for charging of the capacitor to approximately $R_C C/\beta_{F2}$, where β_{F2} is the forward short-circuit current gain of the second transistor. However, the emitter follower is ineffective in discharging the capacitor because it cannot support emitter current of reversed polarity. For this reason the diode is added, thus bypassing the emitter follower during discharge. With this circuit, both transition times can be reduced to a fraction of a time constant.

* If the response times are comparable, the transient response can be evaluated by using charge-control techniques. See Problem P2.5.

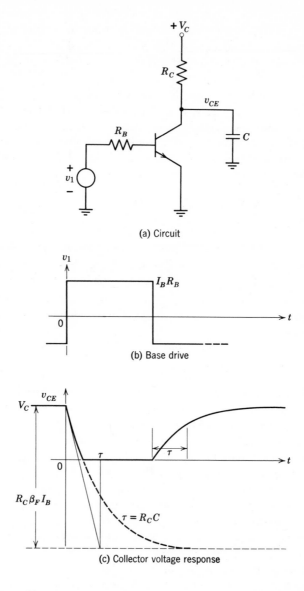

(a) Circuit

(b) Base drive

(c) Collector voltage response

Fig. 2.10. Transient response of an overdriven amplifier with a capacitive load.

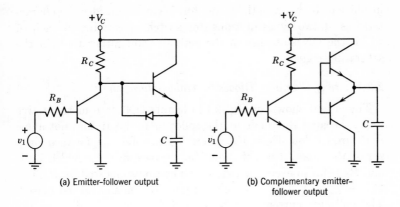

(a) Emitter-follower output   (b) Complementary emitter-
                                    follower output

Fig. 2.11. Circuits which provide large output currents during both transitions.

An alternate arrangement which uses a pair of complementary transistors in an output emitter follower is shown in Fig. 2.11*b*. In this circuit the capacitor is charged through the upper transistor and discharged through the lower one. Current gain is provided on both charge and discharge, and the rise and fall times are reduced accordingly.

2.2 NONSATURATING CIRCUITS

As indicated in the preceding section, the stored excess charge which results when the ON state of a transistor switch lies in the saturation region causes pulse distortion. Because this distortion appears as a widening of the pulse, it limits the maximum rate at which the switch may be operated. Although the unfortunate consequences of stored excess charge may be alleviated by shaping the drive which is applied to the switch, storage delay cannot be completely eliminated in practical saturating switches because the peak turn-off current is circuit limited.

Several circuit arrangements which prohibit saturation of the transistors have been developed. In general, these circuits avoid saturation in one of two ways; either they use diode clamps to limit the collector-base voltage so that the collector junction cannot become forward biased, or they control the ON-state collector current at a value for which the drop across the load resistance is insufficient to saturate the transistor. We now consider the characteristics of two types of transistor switching circuits, in each of which the ON state lies in the active region rather than in the saturation region.

2.2.1 *Use of Clamping Diodes to Avoid Saturation*

The circuit shown in Fig. 2.12a has its ON state in the active region because the diode at the collector terminal does not allow v_2 to drop below $V_S - V_F$, where V_F denotes the forward drop across the diode. Even if the ON-state base drive provided by v_1 and R_B is far in excess of that which can be supported by R_C, i.e., $(V_C - V_S + V_F)/R_C$, the collector junction remains reverse biased. The collector current increases to $\beta_F I_B$, where I_B denotes the ON-state base current, and the extra collector current appears in the clamp diode.

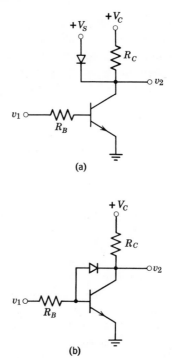

(a)

(b)

Fig. 2.12. Two circuits which use diodes to avoid saturation.

This circuit arrangement is seldom used in practice to achieve a nonsaturating switch. The extra power supply voltage which is required is awkward, and the maximum repetition rate may be limited by charge storage effects anyway—charge storage in the transistor as q_F and in the forward biased clamp diode. The circuit shown in Fig. 2.12b is a more practical way of avoiding saturation of the transistor. The diode becomes forward biased as the transistor leaves the active region, thereby shunting the excess base current through the diode into the collector loop, and preventing a large value of q_R. Although charge is stored in the diode, that device usually recovers faster than a saturated transistor.

2.2.2 *Current-Mode Circuits*

It is generally impossible to design nonsaturating switching circuits in which saturation is avoided by controlling the base current. The common-emitter short-circuit current gain β_F varies from unit to unit far too much to permit accurate control of the ON-state collector current by means of the base current.

On the other hand, the collector current can be controlled, thereby preventing saturation, by designing the switching circuit so that the *emitter* current in the ON state is determined by the circuit and is essentially independent of the base drive. Circuits which use this design philosophy are called *current-mode* logic circuits (CML). A simple form of a CML circuit is shown in Fig. 2.13a.

The fixed current I_O provided by the current source divides between the transistor and the diode in a manner determined by the input voltage v_1. If v_1 is less than the reference potential V_R, the transistor is cut off and essentially all of I_O flows in the diode. The circuit is in the OFF state and the output voltage v_2 is approximately equal to the collector supply voltage V_C. As the input voltage increases, the transistor begins to conduct and the current I_O splits between the diode and transistor. When v_1 exceeds the reference potential V_R by a small margin, the diode is reverse biased and all of I_O flows in the transistor and load. This is the ON state of the circuit, and it is characterized by an output voltage of $V_C - I_O R_C$ (for no external load). The fixed current I_O is "steered" to either the transistor or the diode by the input voltage v_1. This behavior is summarized by the static transfer characteristic shown in Fig. 2.13b.

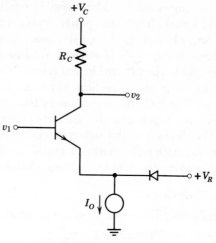

(a) Elementary circuit

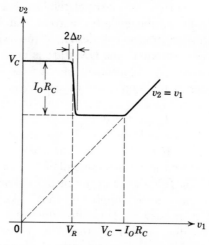

(b) Static transfer characteristic

Fig. 2.13. A current-mode logic circuit.

The range of input voltage over which the transition from off to on occurs, designated as $2\Delta v$ on the static transfer characteristic, is quite narrow. Voltage changes of only a few tenths of a volt suffice to steer the current from the diode to the transistor.

The upward break in the characteristic at $v_1 = V_C - I_O R_C$ occurs when the transistor saturates. Practical *CML* circuits are forced to operate below this point by restrictions on the range of the input voltage.

In practice, the current source is replaced by a resistor and a negative voltage source. This modification causes the static transfer characteristic to have a small positive slope in the region corresponding to the ON state. Also, the diode which supports the constant current in the OFF state of the circuit is frequently replaced by a second transistor. These modifications, which are illustrated in Fig. 2.14, make available two *complementary* outputs (and an additional input at the second base if desired). Consequently, this circuit, which is the basic building block of all current-mode logic circuits, can be used either as an inverter or as a noninverting amplifier.

The element values shown in Fig. 2.14 are reasonable ones for practical *CML* circuits. The values shown for the output variables

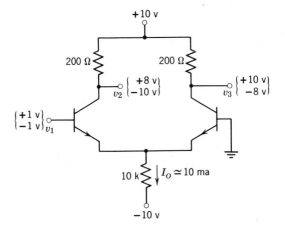

Fig. 2.14. A *CML* circuit which provides complementary outputs. The voltages in brackets correspond to the states of the transistors; the upper voltages occur when the left transistor is on, the lower voltages occur when the left transistor is off.

are approximate, and are based on the assumption that the current switched between transistors is constant at 10 ma. Actually the current in the emitter resistor is slightly different in one state than in the other (see Problem P2.6).

The values of the input and output variables shown in Fig. 2.14 illustrate one inconvenient aspect of *CML* circuits; the voltage levels which correspond to the binary values of the *output* variable differ from the voltage levels at the *input*. Consequently, *CML* circuits cannot be coupled directly.

2.2.3 *Coupling Methods for CML Circuits*

The mismatch of dc levels referred to in the preceding section and illustrated in Fig. 2.14 can be accommodated in several ways when one *CML* circuit is used to drive a second (perhaps through diode logic gates).

One coupling arrangement, which uses zener diodes, is shown in Fig. 2.15a. The dc level of the output voltage v_2 is shifted downward with respect to the dc level of the collector voltage v_3 by an amount equal to the reverse breakdown voltage of the zener diode. The voltage difference between levels is determined by the collector load resistors and by the constant current which is steered to one or the other transistor. Consequently the output levels can be made to correspond directly to the input levels, if desired, by choosing the load resistors and the zener diode appropriately. If the signals at both collectors of the *CML* circuit are used, zener diode level-changing circuits can, of course, be used on both sides.

Current-mode switching circuits can be coupled directly by using the complementary properties of *npn* and *pnp* transistors, as shown in Fig. 2.15b. If the reference levels V_{R1} and V_{R2} are properly chosen, the output levels of the second *CML* circuit (v_2) will be compatible with the levels of the input voltage v_1. While two inverters would not normally be cascaded directly as in this circuit, but would be separated by one or more stages of other logic, the general technique of complementary coupling is illustrated by this circuit.

2.2.4 *Transient Response of CML Circuits*

Current-mode switching circuits are capable of increased rates of operation when compared with saturating circuits constructed

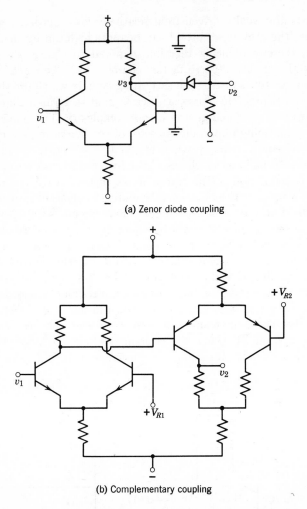

(a) Zenor diode coupling

(b) Complementary coupling

Fig. 2.15. Coupling circuits for use with current-mode logic.

with the same transistors. This relative advantage arises principally because the storage delay time (which inevitably accompanies an ON state in the saturation region) is avoided. Furthermore, *CML* circuits generally operate with small voltage swings and high collector currents, so that the required changes in space-charge-layer charges can be accomplished more rapidly. Finally, these circuits are usually driven from relatively low-impedance sources so that the peak base current can be quite high during changes of state, thereby reducing the time required to change the excess charge in the base. These factors combine to make *CML* circuits two to five times faster than saturating circuits which use comparable transistors. Of course, a price is paid in terms of increased power dissipation and greater circuit complexity. The latter factor is of diminishing importance in view of the increasing use of integrated circuit technology, which makes it possible to add transistors to a digital building block with little increase in cost.

The calculation of the transient response of a *CML* circuit is more complicated than the corresponding analysis of a saturating switch, simply because the current-mode circuit is driven from a very low-impedance source. Consequently, the base current is *not* determined solely by the parameters of the driving circuit, and the transistor cannot generally be regarded as current-controlled.

We can illustrate the issues involved in transient analysis, and can obtain a feeling for the nature of the response times, by considering the two-transistor circuit shown in Fig. 2.16. We assume that the Thévenin equivalent source voltage changes abruptly at $t = 0$ from ΔV below the reference voltage to ΔV above the reference, thereby initiating a transient which concludes when

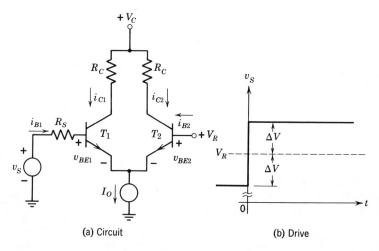

(a) Circuit   (b) Drive

Fig. 2.16. Circuit used in evaluation of transient response.

the current I_O has switched from transistor 2 to transistor 1. We are interested in the time required for this change to occur; this time is the rise time of one collector current and the fall time of the other collector current. We assume that the transistors are identical and are characterized by a forward charge-control parameter τ_F. Since we are interested in fast transients, we will neglect the effects of recombination in the base. Finally, we assume that the base current is always small compared with the collector current.

As a consequence of this last assumption, the circuit constrains the sum of the collector currents to be constant,

$$i_{C1} + i_{C2} = I_O \tag{2.4}$$

while the charge-control model, with space-charge-layer charges and the recombination component of the base current neglected, requires

$$i_{B1} = \tau_F \frac{di_{C1}}{dt} \tag{2.5a}$$

$$i_{B2} = \tau_F \frac{di_{C2}}{dt} \tag{2.5b}$$

Consequently the base currents must be equal and opposite

$$i_{B1} = -i_{B2} \tag{2.6}$$

Kirchhoff's voltage law requires, for the base-to-base loop

$$v_S - V_R = v_{BE1} - v_{BE2} + R_S i_{B1} \tag{2.7}$$

Finally, the charge-control model, which assumes that the charge distributions that correspond to q_F and q_R are triangular under dynamic as well as static conditions, yields the following relationships between the instantaneous emitter-base voltages and the instantaneous collector currents (we have neglected constant terms which correspond to I_{CS}):[*]

$$i_{C1} = \alpha_F I_{ES}(e^{q v_{BE1}/kT} - 1) \tag{2.8a}$$

$$i_{C2} = \alpha_F I_{ES}(e^{q v_{BE2}/kT} - 1) \tag{2.8b}$$

[*] PEM, Sec. 10.3. These equations are less accurate than Eqs. 2.5, and are the weak link in this analysis of transient response. Nevertheless, they lead to a result which is significantly better than that which would be obtained if the emitter-base drops were assumed to be constant.

These seven equations can be reduced to a single nonlinear differential equation which can be integrated to yield the base and collector currents as functions of time. Although it is not feasible to obtain an analytic solution, numerical integration of the differential equation is straightforward.

To illustrate the general nature of the transient response, we have evaluated $i_{C1}(t)$ and $i_{B1}(t)$ for $\Delta V \cong 7\, kT/q$. This corresponds to a total change in v_S of about 0.35 volts, which suffices to change the collector current in each transistor by more than three orders of magnitude.* The parameter $R_S I_O$ appears in the solution, and we have taken it to be

$$R_S I_O = 100\,\frac{kT}{q} \cong 2.5 \text{ volts} \qquad (2.9)$$

The resulting time dependences of the base current and the collector current are shown in Fig. 2.17. For the parameter values chosen, the 10 to 90% response time of the collector current is about 10 τ_F. Furthermore, the base current exhibits a sharp initial spike, which has little effect on the collector current transient; in other words, the spike carries very little charge. Increases in either the Thévenin equivalent source resistance or the quiescent collector current will increase the response time.

---

* In practice, the input voltage swing is usually much greater than this, to preserve a suitable gap between the states in spite of component and power supply variations. Larger voltage swings do *not* speed up the switching action, and may in fact slow down the transient response by introducing delay time before the OFF transistor moves into the active region.

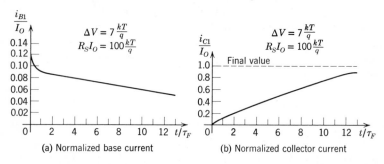

Fig. 2.17. Base and collector current waveforms which result when a *CML* inverter is switched on.

Although this example is oversimplified, it does illustrate the general nature of the transient analysis of current-mode switching circuits. Usually it is necessary to consider the time dependence of the emitter-base voltage because the source resistance is small. In this example the charge-control model was used to relate the emitter-base voltage to the collector current. Inasmuch as this coupling is sharply and unavoidably nonlinear, the differential equations which describe the system are generally nonlinear.

PROBLEMS

P2.1 Verify the transfer characteristic shown in Fig. 2.1*b*. Assume that the transistor emitter junction has a threshold of conduction of 0.4 volt.

P2.2 The parameter values of the inverter circuit shown in Fig. 2.1*a* are *nominal* values. In reality all of these values are subject to some variation. Assume that the resistors may have values within ± 20 of their nominal values, the supply voltages may vary by $\pm 10\%$, and β_F may deviate by $\pm 20\%$ from its nominal value.

(*a*) Determine the *minimum* value of V_A for which $V_B \cong 0$ for all possible actual parameter values. Base your analysis on the least favorable set of parameter values, i.e., consider the worst case.

(*b*) Determine the *maximum* value of V_A for which V_B is approximately equal to the positive supply voltage for all possible actual parameter values. Assume that the transistor is at the threshold of forward conduction when $V_{BE} = 0.4$ volt.

P2.3 This problem is concerned with an inverter circuit which differs from that shown in Fig. 2.1*a* only in that the resistor to the negative supply is removed. Assume that $V_A = 0.1$ volt and estimate the maximum value of the base resistor for which V_{BE} is less than 0.4 volt if $I_{CS} = 2$ na and $I_{ES} = 1$ na. Use $kT/q = 25$ mv.

P2.4 This problem refers to the clamped circuit of Fig. 2.9, and is concerned with the factors which influence the choice of the clamp voltage V_D. Assume for the purposes of this analysis that the diode forward voltage V_F is negligible in comparison with V_D. The circuit is intended to drive loads in both states. The maximum load current has the value I_L.

(*a*) Determine an upper bound for R_C (in terms of V_C, V_D, and I_L) such that the circuit can support the load current of I_L when the transistor is off without the clamp diode opening.

(*b*) Evaluate the collector current I_C when the transistor is on and saturated. Assume that a load current *enters* at the output node (that is, I_L is negative) and use the value of R_C determined in (*a*). Assume $V_{CE}(\text{sat}) \ll V_C$.

(*c*) Sketch and dimension I_C/I_L vs. V_D/V_C for $0 < V_D/V_C < 1$. Note that V_D/V_C should be small if large values of I_C (for fixed I_L) are to be avoided.

P2.5 This problem refers to the circuit of Fig. 2.10a and treats the case in which the internal response time of the current-driven transistor is comparable to the time constant associated with the capacitive load. Assume that $\tau_{BF} = R_C C/3$ and compute, sketch, and dimension the waveforms of the collector current and collector-to-emitter voltage.

P2.6 The circuit of Fig. 2.14 can be characterized by two static transfer characteristics which relate the two output voltages to the input voltage. Using the element values shown, compute, sketch, and dimension these transfer characteristics. Make reasonable assumptions concerning the static behavior of the transistors.

3

Regenerative Switching Circuits

3.0 INTRODUCTION

The switching circuits we considered in Chapter 2 all had in common the feature that the instantaneous state of the circuit, and thus the instantaneous values of the output variables, were determined solely by the input variables at the same instant of time. That is, except for transient time delays associated with the dynamics of state changes, the output of a nonregenerative switching circuit is a single-valued function of the input or inputs at the same time.

We now turn our attention to regenerative switching circuits, which are broadly characterized by having the signal at some point within the circuit determined, in part, by the output variables as well as by the input variables. That is, the output of the circuit is fed back and combined at some point with the input, so that in the signal-flow sense the circuit has a positive feedback path. This positive feedback may result from the external coupling of the output of an amplifier to its own input, or it may be produced by a feedback mechanism internal to the transistor, such as avalanche multiplication. In some cases it may be difficult to characterize the circuit in a manner that makes the feedback stand out, nevertheless, the concept of positive feedback is the one feature that ties together essentially all regenerative switching circuits.

We shall see that these circuits generally have outputs which, as a consequence of the positive feedback, depend not only on the instantaneous values of the inputs but also on their past history. That is, regenerative switching circuits generally exhibit *memory*, and it is this characteristic which makes them useful.

3.1 POSITIVE FEEDBACK IN AMPLIFIERS

We use the simple two-transistor amplifier circuit shown in Fig. 3.1 to illustrate the consequences of positive feedback in amplifiers. In considering signal flow from the input v_I to the output v_O, this amplifier can be regarded as comprised of two common-emitter stages which are directly coupled through the R_{B1}, R_{B2} voltage divider. The two common-emitter stages share a common emitter resistor, and it is this coupling which produces positive feedback. To identify the feedback path, we consider the consequences of an incremental increase in the input voltage v_I. An increase in v_I augments the forward bias on the emitter junction of the first transistor, thereby causing an incremental increase

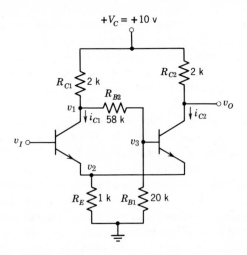

Fig. 3.1. Two-stage amplifier with positive feedback. The designated voltages are defined with respect to ground.

in the collector current, i_{C1}, of that transistor. Consequently both the collector-to-ground voltage v_1 of the first transistor, and the base-to-ground voltage of the second transistor, v_3, decrease. The second transistor operates as an emitter follower which has an additional load resistor in the collector. Therefore, there is an incremental decrease in the emitter-to-ground voltage v_2. This decrease in v_2 causes the forward bias at the emitter of the first transistor to increase even more than would occur as a consequence of the initial increase in v_I alone. If we regard the emitter-base junction of the first transistor as a *summing point*, it is apparent that the signal which is fed back by the emitter follower reinforces the input signal, i.e., the signal at the summing point is caused, by the fed-back signal, to be *greater than* the change in the input voltage alone. This constitutes positive feedback. From the point of view of signal flow *within* the feedback loop, the amplifier is comprised of a common-base stage whose output is coupled back to its own input through an emitter follower.

3.1.1 *Static Transfer Characteristics*

To study in more detail the behavior of this circuit, we shall determine the static transfer characteristic which relates v_O to v_I. We make two assumptions about the dc characteristics of the transistor:

(1) The base current is negligibly small.
(2) The emitter-base voltage in the ON state is zero.

These assumptions do not affect significantly the general nature of our results; they do greatly simplify the analysis.

If the input voltage is small enough, the input transistor is cut off, and the output is independent of the input. We can estimate the maximum value of v_I for which the input transistor is cut off by recognizing that for these element values the second transistor is biased to a point in the active region by the voltage divider comprised of R_{B1}, R_{B2}, and R_{C1}. In view of our first assumption, the base-to-ground voltage of the second transistor is

$$v_3 = V_C \frac{R_{B1}}{R_{B1} + R_{B2} + R_{C1}} \tag{3.1}$$

This value of the voltage v_3 is 2.5 volts for the numerical values shown in Fig. 3.1. Therefore, in accordance with our second assumption, the first transistor is cut off for any value of input voltage less than

$$v_{Ia} = V_C \frac{R_{B1}}{R_{B1} + R_{B2} + R_{C1}} = 2.5 \text{ volts} \qquad (3.2)$$

For input voltages less than this critical value, the output voltage is constant at

$$v_O = V_C - i_{C2}R_{C2} = V_C - v_2 \frac{R_{C2}}{R_E} = 5 \text{ volts} \qquad (3.3)$$

The corresponding portion of the static transfer characteristic terminates at point a in Fig. 3.2.

When the input voltage reaches the critical value defined by Eq. 3.2, the input transistor begins to conduct. Consequently v_1 and v_3 drop, reducing the current in the output transistor. This causes the output voltage to rise toward the 10-volt collector supply voltage. In addition, the emitter voltage drops as the current in the output transistor decreases. The resulting positive feedback tends to increase the forward bias on the input transistor, thereby increasing its collector current still further.

The region of the static transfer characteristic for which *both* transistors are in the active region, terminates when the collector current in the second transistor reaches zero. At this point, the current in the emitter resistor is just equal to the collector current of the first transistor. The collector-to-ground voltage of the first transistor must satisfy the following node equation

$$\frac{V_C - v_1}{R_{C1}} = i_{C1} + \frac{v_1}{R_{B1} + R_{B2}} \qquad (3.4a)$$

Because

$$v_2 = v_1 \frac{R_{B1}}{R_{B1} + R_{B2}}$$

the collector current i_{C1} when i_{C2} is zero is

$$i_{C1} = \frac{v_2}{R_E} = v_1 \frac{R_{B1}}{(R_{B1} + R_{B2})R_E} \qquad (3.4b)$$

The corresponding value of v_I, which is just equal to v_2, is

$$v_{Ic} = V_C \frac{R_{B1}}{R_{B1} + R_{B2} + R_{C1} + (R_{C1}R_{B1}/R_E)} \cong 1.7 \text{ volts} \quad (3.5)$$

The associated value of output voltage is

$$v_O = V_C = 10 \text{ volts} \quad (3.6)$$

since the second transistor is at the edge of cutoff.

Comparison of Eqs. 3.2 and 3.5 shows that v_{Ic} is *less than* v_{Ia}.* Thus the corresponding portion of the static transfer characteristic has a negative slope, as shown in Fig. 3.2. The portion of the transfer characteristic between points a and c must be a straight line because both transistors are in the active region throughout this range of output voltage, and our assumptions about the transistor characteristics imply piecewise-linear behavior.

The shape of the segment ac of the characteristic can also be verified by direct calculation. In developing this analysis, it is necessary to regard v_O as the independent variable and to compute

---

* This is true for any choice of parameters such that $R_{C1}R_{B1}/R_E$ is nonzero. If we had used a more accurate transistor model which accounted for base current and a nonzero emitter-base voltage, the condition necessary for v_{Ic} to be less than v_{Ia} would be more stringent.

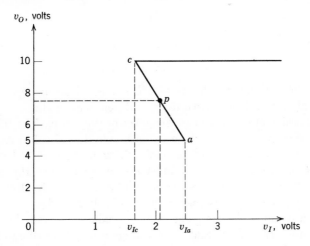

Fig. 3.2. Static transfer characteristic for the amplifier of Fig. 3.1.

the corresponding value of v_I. This procedure avoids ambiguities inasmuch as the transfer characteristic is a single-valued function of v_O but a triple-valued function of v_I for $v_{Ic} < v_I < v_{Ia}$.

We illustrate the analysis of the circuit in the negative-slope region by considering the halfway point at which $v_O = 7.5$ volts (point p in Fig. 3.2). At this point the collector current of the second transistor is

$$i_{C2} = \frac{V_C - v_O}{R_{C2}} = \frac{10 - 7.5}{2 \text{ k}} = 1.25 \text{ ma}$$

The collector current of the first transistor is

$$i_{C1} = \frac{V_C - v_1}{R_{C1}} - \frac{v_1}{R_{B1} + R_{B2}} \qquad (3.7a)$$

However, because of the emitter-follower action, the emitter voltage v_2 is simply related to v_1, as we saw before.

$$v_2 = \frac{R_{B1}}{R_{B1} + R_{B2}} v_1 \cong v_1/4 \qquad (3.7b)$$

Finally, in terms of the collector currents, v_2 is given by

$$v_2 = (i_{C1} + i_{C2})R_E \qquad (3.7c)$$

Simultaneous solution of Eqs. 3.7a, b, and c yields

$$v_2 \cong 2.1 \text{ volts}$$

The corresponding value of the input voltage v_I at point p is thus

$$v_I = v_2 \cong 2.1 \text{ volts}$$

which lies, within the limits of the numerical accuracy of these calculations, midway between the end points v_{Ia} and v_{Ic}.

This calculation illustrates the effect of the feedback in that an *increase* in the output voltage (from 5 volts to 7.5 volts) requires *a decrease* in the input voltage (from 2.5 volts to about 2.1 volts). The negative slope of the transfer characteristic in the region where both transistors are active results from the positive feedback. Throughout this region the feedback provides more than enough signal at the summing point to produce the desired output. Consequently, the external input voltage v_I must *decrease* to bring about an increase in the output voltage. In accordance with the feedback point of view, we can say simply that with both transistors active, the feedback is positive, and the magnitude of the loop transmission is greater than unity.

3.1.2 *Stability Considerations*

As we indicated above, for input voltages in the range

$$v_{Ic} < v_I < v_{Ia}$$

the transfer characteristic is a triple-valued function of v_I. Thus it would appear that the circuit could be at any of *three* different operating points for a given input voltage in this range. We now examine the stability of these operating points and conclude that the point on the segment having negative slope is unstable and thus unattainable in reality.

The two operating points which lie on the flat portions of the transfer characteristic correspond to operation with one or the other of the two transistors cut off, as shown in Sec. 3.1.1. Consequently, the incremental loop transmission at either of these operating points is essentially zero, the feedback path is broken, and the output is disconnected from the input. It follows that these operating points are *stable*.

The operating point which lies on the segment of the transfer characteristic having negative slope corresponds to operation with both transistors active. By directly calculating the loop transmission under these conditions we can draw some important conclusions about the stability of this operating point. We have already indicated that the feedback at midfrequency is *positive*. We will now investigate the magnitude of the loop transmission T, and will find that $|T|$ is greater than unity. Consequently, the circuit in this state has a pole in the right half-plane, and the operating point is unstable. Therefore, any deviation from equilibrium at this operating point causes a transient which *grows* in amplitude with time, thus driving the system out of the region of negative slope in one direction or the other. This operating point is *unstable*, and the system will never equilibrate at this point.

In order to calculate the loop transmission *we assume that v_I* and v_O are constant at an operating point which lies in the region of negative slope, where both transistors are active, and consider the incremental behavior of the system. An appropriate incre-

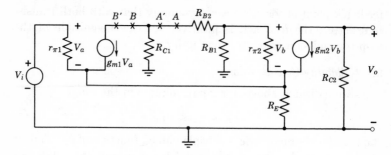

(a) Incremental model of the circuit of Fig. 3.1

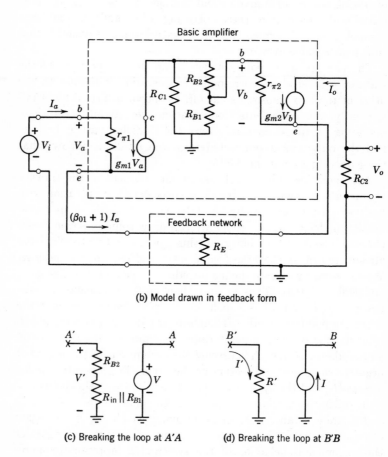

(b) Model drawn in feedback form

(c) Breaking the loop at $A'A$

(d) Breaking the loop at $B'B$

Fig. 3.3. Incremental model for calculating the loop transmission.

mental model of this circuit is shown in Fig. 3.3a. In the model the transistors are represented by elementary common-emitter pi-type models containing only r_π and g_m.

In Fig. 3.3b, the model has been redrawn to emphasize the division of the circuit into two component parts: a basic two-stage unilateral amplifier, and a feedback network which samples (approximately) output current, and sums a feedback voltage with the input voltage. That is, this circuit has *transimpedance feedback*.*

Unfortunately, in this circuit the signal fed *forward* through the feedback path is sufficiently large that it cannot be neglected compared to the signal fed forward through the amplifier, and thus it is not possible to recast this network into the classical feedback form.† However, in accordance with the discussion in MTC, Sec. 3.2.3, it is possible to identify the loop transmission af *regardless* of whether or not we can identify the separate factors a and f in a convenient feedback form. In fact, for the bistable multivibrators to be discussed in Sec. 3.3, there is no recognized "input" terminal, so the feedback form is somewhat arbitrary.

By using the general z-parameter representation of two two-ports connected as in Fig. 3.3b (i.e., the z-parameter equivalent of Fig. 3.10 of MTC) or by direct calculation from Fig. 3.3b, it can be proved that the loop transmission can be found by "breaking the loop" as follows (see Problem P3.9). The loop is broken at any convenient place, and the voltage gain or current gain calculated after a resistor has been added to the output terminals of the resulting amplifier to account for the loading present on these terminals when the loop is closed. Basically we are trying to find out whether the amplifier in Fig. 3.3b can deliver enough output power to supply its own input. Thus, if loading effects are properly accounted for, we can check for instability by showing that *either* the voltage gain, *or* the current gain, *or* the power gain around the loop is greater than unity.

One possible method of breaking the loop is shown in Fig. 3.3c. If the circuit in Fig. 3.3a is broken at points $A'A$, and if a load is

* See R. D. Thornton et al., *Multistage Transistor Circuits* (hereafter referred to as MTC), John Wiley and Sons, Inc. New York, 1965, Sec. 3.2.1.

† More specifically, one of the conditions for reduction of a network into the feedback form, as stated in MTC, Chapter 3, was for transadmittance feedback $|Z_{ff}| \ll |Z_{fa}|$. This condition is not met here.

added from point A' to ground as discussed above, then the magnitude of the loop transmission is equal to V'/V (see Problem P3.1). (The input signal source V_i in Fig. 3.3a is obviously set to zero in this and subsequent loop transmission calculations.) To find the proper load, we note first from Fig. 3.3a that the input resistance of the second transistor is

$$R_{in} = r_{\pi 2} + (1 + \beta_{02})\left(R_E \left\|\frac{r_{\pi 1}}{1 + \beta_{01}}\right)\right. \tag{3.8a}$$

Because $R_E \gg r_{\pi 1}/(1 + \beta_{01})$ for almost all operating points, we can approximate R_{in} by

$$R_{in} \cong r_{\pi 2} + r_{\pi 1}\left(\frac{1 + \beta_{02}}{1 + \beta_{01}}\right) \tag{3.8b}$$

If the incremental current gains β_{01} and β_{02} are approximately equal, R_{in} is approximately $r_{\pi 1} + r_{\pi 2}$. Thus from Fig. 3.3a, the proper loading from point A' to ground in Fig. 3.3a is

$$R = (R_{in}\|R_{B1}) + R_{B2} \tag{3.9}$$

We can now find by inspection of Figs. 3.3a and c that the loop transmission is

$$|T| = \frac{V'}{V} \cong \frac{R_{in}\|R_{B1}}{(R_{in}\|R_{B1}) + R_{B2}} \times \frac{r_{\pi 1}}{r_{\pi 1} + r_{\pi 2}} \times g_{m1}R_{C1}\|R \tag{3.10}$$

We assume $\beta_{01} = \beta_{02} = 100$ and consider an operating condition such that each transistor has a quiescent collector current of about 1 milliampere. Thus $R_{in} = r_{\pi 1} + r_{\pi 2} \cong 5 \, k$. The corresponding magnitude of the loop transmission is approximately 2.6. We conclude that because we have positive feedback and the magnitude of the loop transmission is greater than one, the circuit in this state will be *unstable*.[*] Note, however, that the loop transmission is dependent on the operating points of both transistors through R_{in}; as the quiescent current of either transistor decreases, the corresponding r_π increases, thus reducing the loop transmission.

The loop could just as well be broken at point $B'B$ in Fig. 3.3a. If a current-source drive is used, as in Fig. 3.3d, the calculation is particularly simple because we do not need to calculate resistor

---

[*] In terms of the notation in MTC, positive feedback at midfrequencies implies that $\angle T = 180°$. Thus, the only further condition required for instability is $|T| > 1$.

R' to find the response current I'. Clearly some foresight in selecting an appropriate point to break the loop can simplify the calculations. Points where the "output" resistance of the broken loop is either very high (as in this example) or very low are obviously useful choices (see Problem P3.2).

A third method for calculating the loop transmission involves recognizing that for the flow of signals *around the loop*, the circuit looks like a common-base amplifier driving a common-collector amplifier. The appropriate model is shown in Fig. 3.4. Note that we have now completely suppressed the source V_i in this drawing. Again the loop may be broken in any one of several places. One particularly convenient place, however, is in the common-base model. Specifically, we "break" the dependent source by assuming that the $\alpha_0 I_1$ generator is an independent source $\alpha_0 I_1'$, and calculate the resulting current I_1 flowing in $r_{\pi 1}/\beta_{01}$ (see Problem P3.3). Breaking the loop by making the dependent source independent of its controlling variable is a very convenient technique if the loop can be *completely* broken by making the generator independent *and* if the loading is *not* disturbed by so doing. However, it is not a "universal" technique. A case in point is the circuit in Fig. 3.3a. Making generator $g_{m2}V_b$ independent does not completely break the loop, and making generator $g_{m1}V_a$ independent changes the loading on the input, so extra loading must be introduced just as in our original calculations.

3.1.3 *Apparent Transfer Characteristics*

The preceding discussion has shown that the only stable operating points of the circuit lie on the horizontal segments of the static

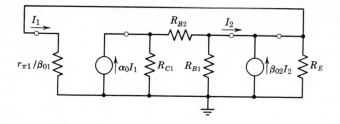

Fig. 3.4. An alternate form of the incremental model.

transfer characteristic. Consequently, observation of the input and output variables of the circuit leads to the conclusion that the circuit has the transfer characteristic shown in Fig. 3.5. The arrows indicate the direction in which the segments can be traversed. When v_I increases from below v_{Ic}, the circuit is in a state defined by $v_O = 5$ volts (transistor 1 is cut off). As v_I increases above v_{Ia} the input transistor enters the active region and the circuit switches regeneratively to the state defined by $v_O = 10$ volts (transistor 2 is cut off). As v_I decreases from above v_{Ia}, similar action occurs and switching takes place at v_{Ic}. The segment ab is always traversed upward while the segment cd is always traversed downward.

For input voltages between v_{Ic} and v_{Ia}, the circuit can be in either state, depending on the past history of the input signal. Thus the circuit exhibits memory in the sense that with $v_I = 2.0$ volts, for example, $v_O = 10$ volts if v_I has been above 2.5 volts more recently than it has been below 1.7 volts, whereas $v_O = 5$ volts if the inverse is true.

3.1.5 *Classes of Regenerative Switching Circuits*

Practical regenerative switching circuits appear in a rich variety of forms which differ significantly in the details of their behavior. Nevertheless, the simple two-stage amplifier with positive feedback which has formed the basis of our discussions in this section can be used to illustrate the several types of regenerative switching circuits.

The circuit of Fig. 3.1 can be used as an *amplitude discriminator* or *trigger circuit*. The output of such a circuit is two-valued in nature, and the output state depends on the static value of the input voltage. This dependence is extremely nonlinear, as demonstrated by the static transfer characteristic of Fig. 3.5. We consider the properties of trigger circuits in Sec. 3.2.

If the input voltage in the circuit of Fig. 3.1 is constant at a value which lies in the range where the circuit can have loop transmission in excess of unity, the circuit is *bistable* in nature. That is, the output voltage can have either of two values, and the state of the circuit can be changed only by applying a perturbation which brings the circuit into the region for which *both* transistors are active.

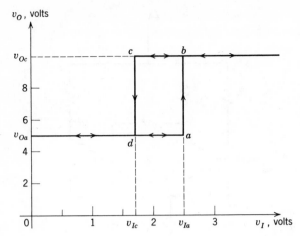

Fig. 3.5. Apparent static transfer characteristic for the amplifier of Fig. 3.1.

A bistable circuit based on the basic amplifier of Fig. 3.1 is shown in Fig. 3.6. The voltage divider comprised of R_1 and R_2 is chosen so that the base-to-ground voltage of the first transistor lies in the range of bistability ($v_{Ic} < v_I < v_{Ia}$ in Fig. 3.5). If the circuit is in the stable state defined by the second transistor being off, it can be *triggered* into the other state by applying a negative-going pulse at the point marked "trigger input".* If the trigger is large enough, the state of the circuit will change regeneratively, and the first transistor will be turned off. In this latter state a positive-going trigger is required to produce a change of state. Bistable circuits are considered in more detail in Sec. 3.3.

The properties of a regenerative switching circuit can be modified by inserting energy-storage elements which suppress one or both of the stable operating points of the circuit. The circuit of Fig. 3.7, which is adapted from our basic circuit by introducing a capacitor into the feedback signal flow path, illustrates the use of an energy-storage element in a regenerative circuit. The resistors R_3 and R_4 are chosen so that the right-hand transistor is operating in the

---

* The distinction between a *trigger circuit* and a *trigger input* is important. A trigger circuit has two stable states, and makes transitions from one to the other when a slowly-changing input signal exceeds or falls below certain critical levels. A trigger input is a fast pulse-like signal which causes a regenerative circuit to change state.

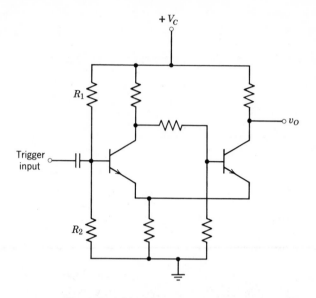

Fig. 3.6. A bistable regenerative circuit.

active region. Resistors R_1 and R_2 are chosen so that the left-hand transistor is off with a reverse-biased emitter junction. This state of the circuit is stable and will persist indefinitely because the loop transmission is zero. The circuit can be triggered into another state, characterized by having the left-hand transistor on and the right-hand transistor off, by applying a positive-going trigger pulse of sufficient amplitude. This trigger pulse moves the first transistor to the edge of conduction and the circuit switches regeneratively to a state defined by having the first transistor on and the second off. The loop transmission is greater than unity during this regenerative transition because the voltage across the capacitor cannot change instantaneously.

The state into which the circuit is switched by the trigger pulse cannot persist indefinitely, however. The voltage on the capacitor changes with time, so that the second transistor approaches the threshold of conduction as its base-to-ground voltage increases with time. When conduction begins in the second transistor, the circuit switches regeneratively back to its original state and remains there until another trigger pulse is applied.

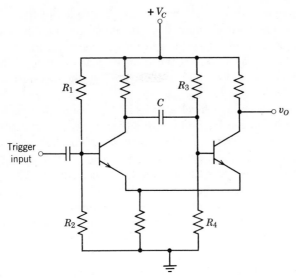

Fig. 3.7. A regenerative circuit in which the introduction of a capacitor produces monostable behavior.

Since this circuit possesses only one stable state it is called a *monostable* circuit. The time spent in the other *metastable* state is controlled by the circuit parameters governing the capacitor discharge. Consequently, monostable circuits are frequently used to generate pulses of prescribed amplitude and duration in response to a trigger pulse. We examine the properties of monostable circuits in more detail in Sec. 3.4.

Energy-storage elements can be introduced in such a way that both states of the circuit are metastable, and persist for a limited time only. Such a circuit, which is said to be *astable*, switches back and forth between the two states at a rate determined by the charge and discharge of the energy storage elements. Circuits of this type are nonlinear oscillators, and are often employed for the generation of periodic waveforms and pulse trains. We examine their properties more thoroughly in Sec. 3.5.

3.2 TRIGGER CIRCUITS

The emitter-coupled amplifier used in Sec. 3.1 as the basis for our discussion of regenerative switching circuits is the transistorized version of the *Schmitt trigger circuit*. The use of the circuit as a amplitude discriminator depends upon the existence of two stable discrete output states and on the control provided by the input voltage, as shown in the transfer characteristic of Fig. 3.5. The operation of the circuit is illustrated by the waveforms shown in Fig. 3.8.

The input voltage level at which the circuit changes state is different for increasing voltages than for decreasing voltages. This input voltage difference is called the *hysteresis* of the trigger circuit. If the purpose of the circuit is simply to register the time at which the input voltage exceeds or falls below certain critical levels in terms of a change of state of the output voltage, the magnitude of the hysteresis is of no consequence. If the purpose of the circuit is to define the time interval for which the input voltage is above a critical threshold level, the hysteresis should be made as small as possible.

Hysteresis in a trigger circuit is concomitant with regenerative switching between states, and cannot be eliminated if the output

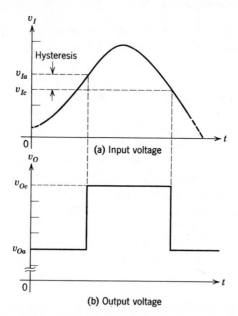

Fig. 3.8. Response of a Schmitt trigger circuit to an input signal.

voltage is to have two quantized levels. The discussion of Sec. 3.1 shows that hysteresis is present whenever there is a region of operation for which both transistors are active and the feedback loop transmission is greater than unity. Thus, such a region is essential if the switching action is to be regenerative.

The magnitude of the hysteresis can be reduced by decreasing the loop transmission. We shall see in the following section that reduced loop transmission causes slower regenerative transitions. Furthermore, if the loop transmission is reduced below the critical value of unity, the circuit behaves simply as a high-gain amplifier having the nonlinear transfer characteristic shown in Fig. 3.9.

3.3 BISTABLE CIRCUITS

A common form of bistable circuit uses two transistors with symmetrical resistive collector-to-base coupling. A circuit of this type, as shown in Fig. 3.10, can be regarded as a two-stage direct-coupled amplifier comprised of common-emitter stages, with positive feedback provided by connecting the output directly to the input.* Bistable circuits are often called *flip-flops.*

There are two methods for determining whether a circuit like that shown in Fig. 3.10 is bistable, and for guiding the design of such circuits. First, we can look directly for the existence of *two*

* A discussion of bistable circuits at an elementary level appears in ECP, Sec. 2.3.5.

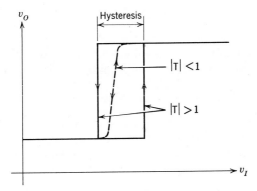

Fig. 3.9. The effect of the loop transmission T on the transfer characteristic of a trigger circuit.

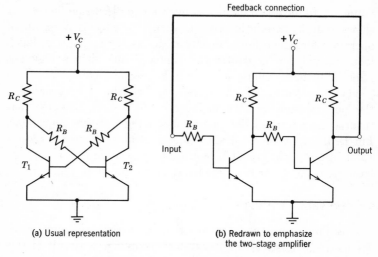

Fig. 3.10. Symmetrical bistable circuit.

stable states, in each of which at least one transistor is *not* in the active region. If these states exist, then the circuit will exhibit bistability. Second, we can determine the incremental loop transmission with both transistors in the active region. The dc constraints imposed by the circuit must, of course, be such that both transistors can be biased simultaneously in the active region. If the loop transmission is greater than unity, regeneration will drive the circuit in one direction or the other until at least one transistor leaves the active region (i.e., becomes cut off or saturated). Consequently, a loop transmission in excess of unity is a necessary condition for bistability. We illustrate these methods of insuring bistability by applying both to the circuit of Fig. 3.10.

3.3.1 *Analysis of the Two Stable States*

Inasmuch as the circuit is symmetric, and since we assume for simplicity that the transistors are identical, we need look for only *one* stable state; the other follows from symmetry. Assume that transistor T_1 is off. The base current of T_2 is then

$$i_{B2} = \frac{V_C - v_{BE}}{R_C + R_B}$$

The collector current of T_2 is

$$i_{C2} = \frac{V_C - v_{CE}}{R_C}$$

Saturation of this transistor is ensured if

$$i_{B2} > \frac{i_{C2}}{\beta_F} \qquad (3.11a)$$

Usually the supply voltage V_C is substantially greater than v_{BE} and v_{CE}. Thus Eq. 3.11a reduces to

$$\beta_F > \frac{R_C + R_B}{R_C} \qquad (3.11b)$$

The circuit configuration insures that for silicon transistors, T_1 will be held OFF if T_2 is saturated, because v_{CE} in saturation is less than v_{BE} at the threshold of conduction (see Secs. 1.2.2 and 2.1.1). Thus, if the condition in Eq. 3.11b is met, our original assumption of T_1 off is validated, and the existence of two stable states is assured. With germanium transistors, particularly at high temperatures, the difference between $V_{CE}(\text{sat})$ and v_{BE} at the threshold of conduction may be too small to ensure reliable operation. Therefore, in such circuits the base is often returned to a supply voltage (negative for *npn* transistors) which guarantees that the emitter junction of one transistor is reverse-biased when the other transistor is saturated.

3.3.2 *Calculation of Incremental Loop Transmission*

The loop transmission calculation is based on an incremental model of the circuit, shown in Fig. 3.11. Since we are not now investigating the speed of the regenerative switching action, we have omitted the capacitances in the hybrid-π transistor model. Furthermore, we have neglected in the model the consequences of base-width modulation. From the feedback point of view, the arrangement shown in Fig. 3.11 constitutes *transadmittance feedback*.* The "output," which appears at terminals $o\text{-}o'$ is coupled back to the "input" terminals $i\text{-}i'$ by the feedback admittance $1/R_B$.

* MTC, Sec. 3.2.1.

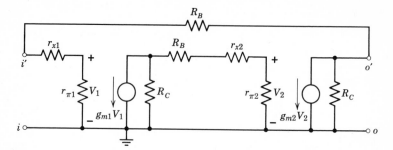

Fig. 3.11. Incremental model for the bistable circuit of Fig. 3.10.

The loop transmission can be calculated by disconnecting the feedback network at the input terminals and, after accounting for the load on the amplifier input terminal, calculating the current transfer ratio from the amplifier input to the shorted output of the feedback network.

An equivalent procedure for finding the loop transmission is to break the feedback loop at one of the dependent generators, as discussed in Sec. 3.1.2. Specifically, if we assume, in Fig. 3.11, that the right-hand current generator develops a current of $g_{m2}V_2'$ and calculate the resulting value of V_2, the loop transmission is simply V_2/V_2'. To simplify the calculations, we assume that R_B is much bigger than r_x. On this basis, the loop transmission becomes

$$\frac{V_2}{V_2'} = \left(\frac{-g_{m2}R_C}{R_C + r_{\pi 1} + R_B}\right) r_{\pi 1} \left(\frac{-g_{m1}R_C}{R_C + r_{\pi 2} + R_B}\right) r_{\pi 2} \quad (3.12a)$$

For r_π small compared to $(R_C + R_B)$, this reduces to

$$\frac{V_2}{V_2'} = \left(\frac{\beta_0 R_C}{R_C + R_B}\right)^2 \quad (3.12b)$$

Observe that if the above approximations are valid, the loop gain is a function of current level only through the variation in β_0 with current. However, the loop gain falls at both ends of the active region because one r_π increases, and is no longer negligible compared with $R_B + R_C$. The condition that the loop gain given by Eq. 3.12b be greater than unity is seen to be identical to the condition imposed by Eq. 3.11b for the existence of two stable states.

3.3.3 *Conditions for Bistability*

We are now in a position to state with some precision the necessary and sufficient conditions to assure bistable operation of a multivibrator. These conditions can best be explained by treating the bistable multivibrator as two coupled inverters, as was done in ECP, Sec. 2.3.5. The results of that analysis are summarized in Fig. 3.12. The multivibrator positive feedback loop has been broken at one collector as shown in Fig. 3.12a, and the static transfer curve v_{C2} versus v_{B1} plotted, as in b. (We assume that $R_B \gg R_C$, so that no "load" is required on the v_{C2} terminals to duplicate the closed-loop condition.) Closing the loop in Fig. 3.12a by adding the dotted connection corresponds in b to an additional constraint $v_{C2} = v_{B1}$, a 45° line in the v_{C2}-v_{B1} plane. For the case

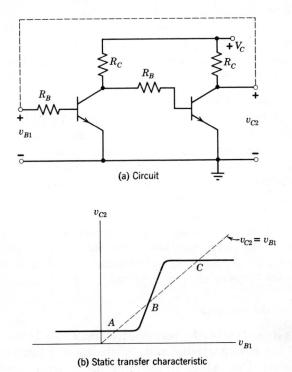

(a) Circuit

(b) Static transfer characteristic

Fig. 3.12. Multivibrator drawn as two inverters with feedback.

shown, there are three possible operating points, and, as discussed in ECP, points A and C are stable, whereas B is a point of unstable equilibrium. The circuit can be made to change state from A to C or vice versa by application of a suitable triggering signal.

One way of proving bistability thus involves proving the existence of the two stable operating points A and C. From the geometry of Fig. 3.12b, it is clear that a second method of proving bistability is to show that at point B, the slope of the v_{C2} versus v_{B1} characteristic is greater than unity, i.e., the incremental loop transmission at this point is greater than one. These same conditions stated in more general terms are:

(1) A *necessary and sufficient condition* for bistable operation is the existence of two stable dc circuit states, in each of which at least one transistor is *not* in the active region.

(2) An alternative necessary and sufficient condition for bistability is that the incremental loop transmission at dc with both transistors in the active region be greater than unity at one possible dc operating point. (This operating point will thus be unstable.)

It is important when applying condition (2) to check in addition that one or the other transistor is in fact saturated at points A and C. If this condition is not met, regeneration will drive the circuit toward one or the other of the extremes of the domain of active-region operation, but regeneration may terminate before either device is driven *out* of the active region. While such a circuit is bistable in the formal sense, the outputs are likely to be poorly quantized, and operation is likely to depend critically on the parameters of the transistors. Because ultimately we must check for the existence of two stable states not in the active region in either (1) or (2), for most applications it is easier to check for bistability by using the first condition.

3.3.4 *Switching Speed*

The dynamics of the regenerative transitions between stable states are governed principally by the speed limitations of the transistors. Calculation of the switching interval which begins when a trigger pulse moves the system into the active region of large loop transmission and terminates when one transistor is driven out of the active region, presents a difficult problem of nonlinear analysis which we will not undertake. We can, however, gain considerable insight into the parameters which influence the switching speed by analysing the circuit of Fig. 3.13 using a simplified charge-control model which neglects space-charge capacitance effects. We assume that the transistors, which are both in the active region, are identical and are characterized by the forward charge-control parameters τ_{BF} and τ_F.

The external circuit can be described by two loop equations if we assume that the emitter-base drops can be neglected. These equations are

$$V_C - i_{B2}R_B - (i_{C1} + i_{B2})R_C = 0 \qquad (3.13a)$$

$$V_C - i_{B1}R_B - (i_{C2} + i_{B1})R_C = 0 \qquad (3.13b)$$

The transistors can be described by the charge-control equations. For T_1 we have, from Eqs. 1.2

$$i_{C1} = \frac{q_{F1}}{\tau_F}$$

$$i_{B1} = \frac{q_{F1}}{\tau_{BF}} + \frac{dq_{F1}}{dt}$$

On eliminating q_{F1} between these two equations, we obtain

$$i_{B1} = \frac{i_{C1}}{\beta_F} + \tau_F \frac{di_{C1}}{dt} \qquad (3.14a)$$

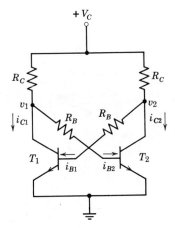

Fig. 3.13. Circuit used in analysis of transition interval.

where we have used $\beta_F = \tau_{BF}/\tau_F$. Similarly, for T_2, we obtain

$$i_{B2} = \frac{i_{C2}}{\beta_F} + \tau_F \frac{di_{C2}}{dt} \tag{3.14b}$$

Elimination of i_{B1} and i_{B2} from Eqs. 3.13 and 3.14 yields the following pair of coupled differential equations:

$$i_{C1} + \frac{1}{\sqrt{A}} \left(i_{C2} + \tau_{BF} \frac{di_{C2}}{dt} \right) = \frac{V_C}{R_C} \tag{3.15a}$$

$$\frac{1}{\sqrt{A}} \left(i_{C1} + \tau_{BF} \frac{di_{C1}}{dt} \right) + i_{C2} = \frac{V_C}{R_C} \tag{3.15b}$$

where the constant A is the low-frequency loop transmission of the circuit (see Sec. 3.3.2, except here we use the large-signal parameter β_F in place of β_0).

$$A = \left(\frac{\beta_F R_C}{R_C + R_B} \right)^2 \tag{3.16}$$

The time dependence of the collector currents during the transition interval is governed by the homogeneous equations that result when the right sides of Eqs. 3.15 are set equal to zero. To find the natural frequencies, we assume that the currents are complex exponentials, yielding the following relations for the complex amplitudes.

$$I_{c1} + \frac{I_{c2}}{\sqrt{A}} (1 + s\tau_{BF}) = 0 \tag{3.17a}$$

$$\frac{I_{c1}}{\sqrt{A}} (1 + s\tau_{BF}) + I_{c2} = 0 \tag{3.17b}$$

The characteristic equation is thus

$$1 - \left(\frac{1 + s\tau_{BF}}{\sqrt{A}} \right)^2 = 0 \tag{3.18}$$

and the natural frequencies are

$$s_1 = \frac{\sqrt{A} - 1}{\tau_{BF}} \tag{3.19a}$$

$$s_2 = - \left(\frac{\sqrt{A} + 1}{\tau_{BF}} \right) \tag{3.19b}$$

Note that for a transmission A greater than unity, the circuit has one pole in the right half-plane and another in the left half-plane. The characteristic mode associated with the natural frequency at s_2 in the left half of the s-plane is, in accordance with Eqs. 3.17, described by

$$I_{c1} = I_{c2} \qquad (3.20a)$$

That is, in this *symmetric* mode the collector currents both decay exponentially with time. On the other hand, the mode associated with the pole at $s = s_1$ in the right half-plane is *antisymmetric* and is characterized by

$$I_{c1} = -I_{c2} \qquad (3.20b)$$

For this mode, the collector currents behave in a "see-saw" manner and grow exponentially with time. This corresponds to the physical situation in which one collector current is increasing at an exponentially growing rate toward saturation while the other collector current is decreasing at an exponentially growing rate toward cutoff. Thus the antisymmetric mode corresponds to the transition between states.

Assuming now that the loop transmission A is much greater than unity, we find from Eqs. 3.20 that the complete *homogeneous* solutions for the collector currents as a function of time are

$$i_{C1} \cong K_1 e^{\sqrt{A}t/\tau_{BF}} + K_2 e^{-\sqrt{A}t/\tau_{BF}} \qquad (3.21a)$$

$$i_{C2} \cong -K_1 e^{\sqrt{A}t/\tau_{BF}} + K_2 e^{-\sqrt{A}t/\tau_{BF}} \qquad (3.21b)$$

The first term in each equation invariably dominates every transition because it grows with time, whereas the second term decays to zero. It is clear from Eqs. 3.21 that rapid switching requires that τ_{BF} be small, and the loop gain be large.

The switching speed of a bistable circuit can be increased by adding a speed-up capacitor in parallel with each of the cross-coupling resistors. This has the effect of increasing the loop transmission for high rates of change, thereby making possible more rapid changes of the internal charge of the transistors.

3.3.5 *Triggering Considerations*

A bistable switching circuit can be made to change state by means of a trigger pulse which brings the system into a condition for which both transistors are active, and thus gets the seesaw transition started in the proper direction. Trigger pulses can be applied to the base or the collector, and can be of such polarity as to turn the ON transistor OFF, or vice versa. One example of base triggering is shown in Fig. 3.14a. If T_1 is on, the circuit can be triggered into the other stable state by applying a negative-going pulse at input a. This trigger pulse must satisfy several constraints. First, it must have sufficient amplitude to remove the saturation charge q_s from the ON transistor, and it must be of sufficient duration to hold this transistor out of saturation long enough for the second transistor to arrive at the threshold of conduction, at which time regeneration will take over. Second, the source impedance of the circuit which supplies the trigger pulse must be large enough so that the loading which it imposes does not reduce the loop transmission to less than unity, which would have the effect of preventing a *regenerative* transition from one state to the other. Although the circuit will change state under such conditions, it will not switch in the fast, definitive manner characteristic of regenerative switching.

A potentially ambiguous situation occurs if trigger pulses are applied to both bases of the bistable circuit simultaneously. This ambiguity can be eliminated by gating the trigger inputs, as shown in Fig. 3.14b. The OFF transistor reverse biases the diode connected to its base, thereby preventing passage of a trigger pulse. On the other hand, the diode at the base of the ON transistor is slightly forward biased, so that a trigger pulse applied to that side of the circuit is unimpeded.

The arrangement of Fig. 3.14b is used to realize a scale-of-two counter. The two trigger inputs are tied together so that each trigger pulse causes the circuit to change state. Thus, both output voltages pass through a full cycle *once* for every *two* input pulses. A cascade of such circuits can be used to count pulses on the binary number scale.

3.3.6 *Complementary Bistable Circuits*

There are, of course, many other forms of two-transistor bistable circuits. One variation, which uses the complementary properties of *pnp* and *npn* transistors is shown in Fig. 3.15. One stable state of this circuit is characterized by having both transistors on; the

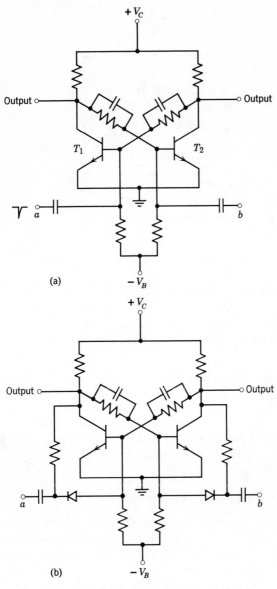

(a)

(b)

Fig. 3.14. Triggering of bistable circuits.

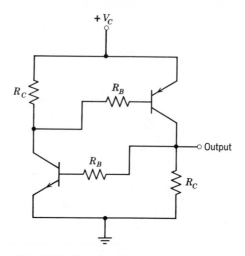

Fig. 3.15. Complementary bistable circuit.

other state has both transistors off. This circuit is particularly useful if the application is such that the circuit spends much more time in the OFF state than in the ON state. Under this condition the power consumption can be made very low.

3.4 MONOSTABLE CIRCUITS

A bistable switching circuit can be made to exhibit monostable behavior if one equilibrium state is suppressed. Two typical circuit arrangements are illustrated in Fig. 3.16a and b. Each of these circuits is capable of two modes of operation, which differ in the choice of the stable state.

3.4.1 *The Cross-Coupled Circuit*

The most common mode of operation of the cross-coupled circuit, as shown in Fig. 3.16a is one in which R_{B2} is chosen to hold T_2 in saturation in the stable state. The resistive cross-coupling provided by R_{B1} then holds T_1 off. If a trigger pulse brings the circuit into a condition in which both transistors are active, regenerative switching action will occur, and the circuit will switch to a metastable state defined by having T_2 off and T_1 on. During this

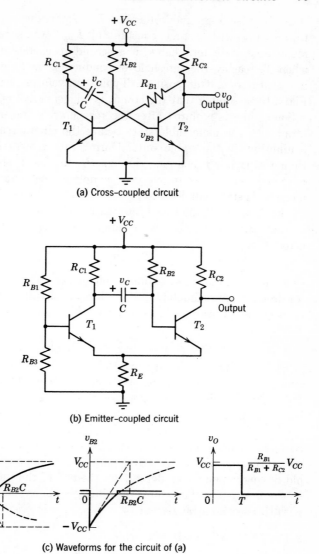

(a) Cross-coupled circuit

(b) Emitter-coupled circuit

(c) Waveforms for the circuit of (a)

Fig. 3.16. Circuits which are capable of monostable behavior.

state the base-to-ground voltage of T_2 is increasing exponentially toward V_{CC} with a time constant of $R_{B2}C$. Consequently, the metastable state terminates in a second regenerative transition when T_2 reaches the threshold of conduction, i.e., when v_{B2} is a few tenths of a volt positive. Typical waveforms are shown in Fig. 3.16c assuming that the circuit is triggered at $t = 0$.

Some time is required after the regenerative transition which terminates the metastable state before the circuit reaches static equilibrium in the stable state. During this *recovery interval* the timing capacitor is charging through R_{C1} to V_{CC}. If the circuit is triggered before this recovery is complete, the duration of the metastable state will decrease.

The duration of the timed interval is governed by the charging of the capacitor C. Before the circuit is triggered, the voltage across C is

$$v_C \cong V_{CC} \tag{3.22}$$

Consequently, the base-to-ground voltage v_{B2} of the second transistor drops to approximately $-V_{CC}$ when the circuit switches. Since v_{B2} is heading toward $+V_{CC}$ the metastable state ends after a time T, given by

$$T \cong R_{B2}C \ln 2 \cong 0.69 R_{B2}C \tag{3.23}$$

The cross-coupled circuit can also be biased so that in the stable state T_2 is off and T_1 is on. Such an arrangement is shown in Fig. 3.17a. In this mode of operation the timing capacitor supplies base current for the ON transistor in the metastable state, and the timed interval ends when the base current falls below the level required to maintain saturation. This condition usually depends more critically on the transistor parameters than does the threshold of conduction which determines the end of the timed interval in the first mode. Therefore, the timing stability may be poorer with this second arrangement.

3.4.2 *The Emitter-Coupled Circuit*

The emitter-coupled circuit likewise has two modes of operation. As the circuit is shown in Fig. 3.16b, in the stable state T_1 is off and T_2 is on. When the circuit is triggered into the metastable state, T_2 is cut off, and the timed interval ends when the base-to-emitter voltage of this transistor reaches the threshold of conduction.

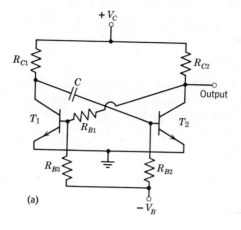

(a)

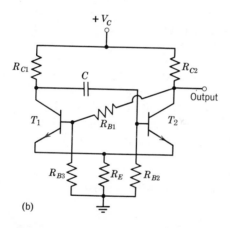

(b)

Fig. 3.17. Monostable circuits in which the current in the timing capacitor is directly influenced by the transistor characteristics.

In the alternate (less common) mode of operation illustrated in Fig. 3.17b, the transistor which is on during the metastable state is supplied with base current through the timing capacitor. This circuit arrangement has the disadvantage that neither collector voltage is constant during the timed interval, so the circuit does not produce a rectangular output pulse.

3.4.3 *Conditions for Monostable Behavior*

It follows from the preceding discussion that the conditions which *together* are necessary and sufficient for monostable behavior of a circuit are:

(1) With the capacitor(s) removed, there must exist only one stable state, in which at least one transistor is out of the active region, *and*

(2) The dc coupling network must be such that both transistors can be in the active region at the same time, *and*

(3) In this active state the magnitude of the incremental loop transmission at some frequency must be greater than unity and the feedback must be positive to insure regenerative behavior.

If these conditions are met, the existence of a metastable state is ensured, and the circuit will exhibit monostable behavior.

It is generally a simple matter to check a circuit such as that in Fig. 3.16a for satisfaction of these requirements. The first requirement is concerned with the steady-state dc bias only, and thus can be applied to the circuit in Fig. 3.16a with the capacitor C removed. The second condition as applied to this circuit requires that there is some dc voltage V_{B2} for which both T_1 and T_2 are in the active region. If this condition is met, then a calculation must be made with the incremental active-region model with capacitor C *shorted* to insure that the feedback is positive and that the magnitude of the loop transmission is greater than unity.

3.5 ASTABLE CIRCUITS

3.5.1 *Circuit Arrangement*

A regenerative switching circuit that has no stable state and thus continuously switches back and forth between two metastable states is called a *free-running* or *astable* multivibrator. Any circuit which is monostable can be made to exhibit astable behavior by adjusting the bias and dc coupling so that both transistors are in the active region when the energy storage element is disabled. For example, the cross-coupled circuit of Fig. 3.16a can be made astable by increasing R_{B2} so that with C removed, T_2 is biased in the active region, and by adjusting R_{B1} and R_{B3} so that T_1 is simultaneously in the active region. When the timing capacitor is reconnected, the positive feedback drives the circuit out of the quasilinear region into one saturated state. However, this condition cannot persist because the capacitor charge changes, letting the circuit relax toward the steady state in which both transistors are active. Thus, the circuit eventually enters the active region and undergoes a regenerative transition through the quasilinear region into the second saturated state, where it resides for a time in a second metastable state.

Although astable behavior is clearly possible with a single timing element, practical circuits are seldom made this way. Such a circuit functions properly only if the bias networks and the dc coupling between stages hold *both* transistors in the active region when the loop is broken by removing the capacitor, and it may be difficult to guarantee that this condition is met for the worst-case variations of component and transistor tolerances. For this reason, most astable circuits employ two capacitors, which permit the bias conditions on the two transistors to be set independently. Figure 3.18 shows examples of cross-coupled and emitter-coupled configurations.

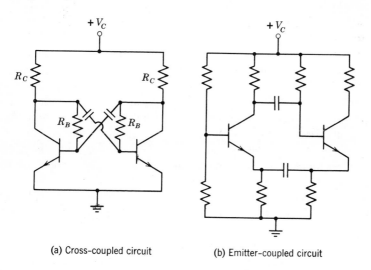

(a) Cross-coupled circuit   (b) Emitter-coupled circuit

Fig. 3.18. Astable multivibrator circuits.

3.5.2 *Conditions for Astable Operation*

The two conditions which *together* are necessary and sufficient to insure astable operation of a circuit are:

(1) The dc operating point of the circuit with the capacitors removed must be such that both transistors are in the active region, *and*

(2) In this active region the magnitude of loop transmission must be greater than unity at some nonzero frequency to insure regenerative action and *less* than unity at dc to *prevent* bistable operation.

Application of these conditions to a specific circuit is again quite simple. For example, it is clear that with the capacitors removed in the circuit in Fig. 3.18a, the transistors will be biased in the active region. If the first condition is satisfied, then a calculation must be made on the active-region incremental model with the coupling capacitors shorted to insure that the loop transmission is greater than unity. The loop transmission at dc for this circuit is clearly zero, so the final condition is satisfied, thereby insuring astable behavior.

3.6 SUMMARY OF CONDITIONS FOR BISTABLE, MONOSTABLE, OR ASTABLE OPERATION

In Secs. 3.3.3, 3.4.3, and 3.5.2 we have stated the necessary and sufficient conditions to insure either bistable, monostable, or astable operation of a multivibrator circuit. To conclude the discussion of multivibrators, it is appropriate to intercompare these conditions to facilitate classification of a given circuit into one of these three subclasses. This intercomparison is done in terms of *necessary* conditions only. The precise statements of *necessary and sufficient* requirements for each type of operation is given in the above-cited subsections.

In comparing the three types of operation it is clear that in all three cases it is necessary to have the magnitude of the loop transmission greater than unity at some frequency in order to insure regenerative action. On the other hand, the conditions on the active-region incremental loop transmission at dc are different for the three circuits, as shown in Table 3.1, and hence can be used to differentiate between the circuits.

TABLE 3.1

Loop Transmission at dc	Circuit
$|T| > 1$	Bistable or monostable
$|T| < 1$	Monostable or astable

The conditions on the number of stable states can also be used as a means of differentiation. This comparison is made in Table 3.2.

TABLE 3.2

Number of Stable States	Circuit
2	Bistable
1	Monostable
0	Astable

As pointed out in Sec. 3.3.3, for proper operation these stable dc states should involve at least one transistor being out of the active region.

3.7 SINGLE-TRANSISTOR REGENERATIVE CIRCUITS

As we have seen in several examples, a basic requirement for any circuit which is to exhibit regenerative switching is that there be a positive feedback loop having a loop transmission with a magnitude greater than unity. Therefore, any amplifier which is to be used as the basis for a regenerative switching circuit must have a voltage gain or a current gain which is positive and in excess of unity when it is operated into a load impedance equal to its input impedance.

It follows from this observation that every single-transistor regenerative switching circuit must contain a transformer. If the transistor is operated in the common-emitter configuration, the loop transmission is greater than unity when the common-emitter stage is loaded by its own input resistance, but a transformer is essential for phase reversal (the incremental gain of a common-emitter stage is negative). Both common-base and common-collector configurations require a transformer, not for phase reversal but to provide current gain in one case and voltage gain in the other.

Single-transistor transformer-coupled circuits can be operated in monostable or astable modes. Bistable operation is not possible because the transformer coupling is not effective for dc.

3.7.1 *Monostable Blocking Oscillators*

Regenerative circuits which contain a single transistor and a transformer are commonly referred to as *blocking oscillators*. The transistor can be used in any of the three possible configurations.

We illustrate the behavior of blocking oscillators by considering the common-emitter circuit shown in Fig. 3.19. In our analysis we employ a drastically over-simplified model of the transformer, characterized by a turns ratio and a magnetizing inductance. In reality, the details of blocking-oscillator performance often depend critically on the transformer, which is seldom linear and which usually has significant leakage inductance.

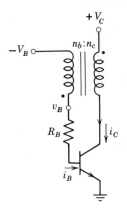

This circuit is normally held in a stable OFF state by the reverse bias voltage V_B. If the transistor is brought to the threshold of conduction by a trigger pulse, a regenerative transition occurs and the transistor switches to a meta-stable saturated ON state.

Fig. 3.19. Monostable common-emitter blocking oscillator.

In this state the voltage across the collector winding of the transistor is approximately V_C. Consequently, the voltage at the bottom of the base winding of the transformer is

$$v_B = \frac{n_b}{n_c} V_C - V_B \qquad (3.24)$$

The base drive current is approximately

$$i_B = \frac{v_B}{R_B} = \frac{\dfrac{n_b}{n_c} V_C - V_B}{R_B} \equiv I_O \tag{3.25}$$

The collector current contains two components. One is the reflected base drive current and is given by $(n_c/n_b)i_B$. The other component results from the charging of the magnetizing inductance of the transformer. This latter component increases with time because there is a constant voltage impressed across the transformer. The metastable state ends when the collector current exceeds that which the transistor can support in saturation with the base drive given by Eq. 3.25. Specifically the metastable state ends when

$$i_C = \beta_F I_O \tag{3.26}$$

At this time the transistor enters the active region, and the resulting regenerative transition switches the system back to the stable OFF state.

The waveforms associated with this simple blocking oscillator are shown in Fig. 3.20. In determining $i_C(t)$ we have assumed that the transformer is essentially linear for the range of currents encountered, and is characterized by a magnetizing inductance L_m. Consequently, the magnetizing component of the collector current increases linearly with time at a rate of V_C/L_m amperes per second. The duration of the metastable state is approximately

$$T = \frac{L_m}{V_C} [\beta_F I_O - \frac{n_c}{n_b} I_O] \tag{3.27}$$

In some blocking oscillator circuits the transformer core is a highly nonlinear permeable material which saturates sharply at a critical flux density. With such a core, the magnetizing component of the collector current increases at a much greater rate when the knee of the magnetization curve is reached, as shown by the dotted line in Fig. 3.20*d*. The duration of the timed interval in such a circuit depends directly on the saturation flux density, but is less critically dependent on the transistor current gain than in a circuit using a nearly linear magnetic material.

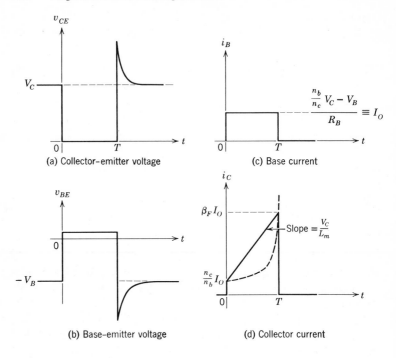

Fig. 3.20. Monostable blocking oscillator waveforms.

   The exponentially decaying spikes which appear on the collector and base voltage waveforms following the transition to the stable OFF state are associated with the decay of the energy stored in the core during the metastable ON state. If the transformer is tightly coupled and has low losses, these spikes can develop very high peak reverse voltages across the transistor junctions. If either junction is driven hard into avalanche, the transistor may be damaged by heating. Consequently, most practical circuits include a diode across one transformer winding to limit the voltage transient on turn-off. Such a diode limiter becomes forward biased when the transistor is turned off, so that the diode absorbs the energy stored in the magnetizing inductance. This circuit modification increases the time required for the circuit to recover between pulses, and thus decreases the maximum permissible triggering rate.

   The output of the blocking oscillator may be taken directly

from the collector, or it may be supplied by a third transformer winding. These circuits are capable of supplying very low impedance loads with high current pulses inasmuch as the ON state base drive can be very high.

Analysis of blocking-oscillator transition intervals is difficult because of the nonlinearities and dynamic properties of both the transistor and transformer. In general, a large loop transmission leads to faster switching. Consequently, a speed-up capacitor is usually inserted across the base current-limiting resistor. Furthermore, leakage inductance in the transformer causes the circuit to switch more slowly by limiting the rate of change of the base current. Consequently, blocking-oscillator transformers must be closely coupled.

3.7.2 *Astable Blocking Oscillators*

The basic blocking oscillator circuit can also be used in an astable or free-running mode by changing the base bias so that the transistor is biased in the active region if the feedback loop is broken. A typical circuit is shown in Fig. 3.21.

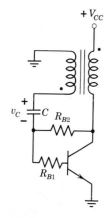

At the beginning of the ON state, the voltage v_C across the capacitor is nearly zero. In the ON state, the transformer supplies base drive through the capacitor and the current-limiting resistor R_{B1}. Consequently, the forward base current decays exponentially toward zero. As in the monostable circuit, the collector current increases with time as a consequence of the magnetizing inductance of the transformer. The ON state ends when the base current is no longer sufficient to support the required collector current with the transistor in saturation. Following the regenerative transition to the OFF state, the emitter junction is reverse-biased by the voltage across the

Fig. 3.21. Free-running blocking oscillator.

capacitor. The circuit is "blocked" in the OFF state until the base-emitter voltage, which is charging toward V_{CC} through R_{B2}, reaches the threshold of conduction, when a regenerative transition to the ON state occurs.

3.8 REGENERATIVE AVALANCHE-MODE CIRCUITS

The common-emitter output characteristics of transistors exhibit negative incremental resistance for operation above the sustaining voltage, as illustrated in Fig. 3.22.* Consequently, one way of using transistors as switches is to operate them in a bistable manner in the avalanche mode (collector voltage in excess of the sustaining voltage). For example, if the transistor whose character-istics are shown in Fig. 3.22 is operated with constant negative base current of magnitude I_a in a circuit described by the load line shown, there are three possible operating points in the avalanche mode, labeled as (1), (2), and (3). Consideration of the imbalance established by a small deviation from these points of equilibrium leads to the conclusion that point (2) is unstable while points (1) and (3) are stable. Consequently a transistor operated in this way can exist at either of the two stable states and can be switched between states by appropriate triggering. The high-voltage, low-

* See also, for example, CLT, Sec. 1.6.2.

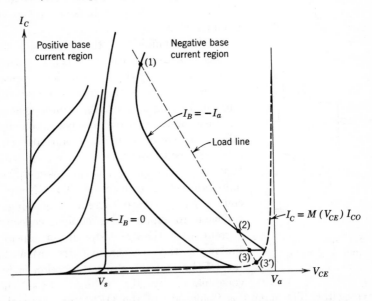

Fig. 3.22. Common-emitter output characteristics of an *npn* transistor show-ing the avalanche region between the sustaining voltage V_s and the avalanche voltage V_a. $M(V_{CE})$ denotes the avalanche multiplication factor.

current point, (3), corresponds to operation in the cut-off region with *both* junctions exhibiting avalanche multiplication. The high-current point, (1), lies in the active region. Although the collector-emitter voltage at point (1) is not small, it is reasonably well defined, so that a bistable transistor in the avalanche mode can be regarded as a switch when viewed at the collector-emitter terminals.

Many practical circuits do *not* impose a rigid constraint on the base current. Rather, in the low-current state, the circuit constrains the emitter-base junction to be slightly reverse-biased rather than in avalanche. In such cases the operating point lies at the intersection of the static load line and the curve which describes the avalanche-multiplied collector saturation current. On this curve, which is shown dashed in Fig. 3.22, the emitter current is approximately zero, and $I_B \cong -I_C$.

The transitions of an avalanche-mode switch between states involve the regenerative build-up or decay of excess charge in the base as well as the changing of space-charge-layer charges. Analysis of the switching time is difficult, and the results are sufficiently complex to be of limited use in circuit design. However, such analysis indicates that a lower bound on the switching time is the forward charge-control parameter τ_F.

A bistable avalanche-mode circuit is shown in Fig. 3.23*a*, and the relevant portions of the collector characteristics appear in Fig. 3.23*b*. In the OFF state the emitter junction is reverse biased by $-V_B$ and both the base current and collector current are very small. In the ON state the emitter junction is forward biased by the flow of avalanche-mode base current through R_B, and the collector current is limited only by the collector load resistance.

The transition from off to on can be initiated by a positive pulse at either the base or the collector. This trigger pulse has the effect of momentarily shifting the load line to the right and thus suppressing the stable OFF state. The circuit switches from on to off when the load line is momentarily displaced below the constant-base-current characteristic by a trigger pulse of opposite polarity. This can be accomplished by a negative-going pulse at the collector, or by a pulse which reverse-biases the emitter junction.

Bistable avalanche-mode circuits are seldom used because the transistor dissipation is very high in the ON state. A much more common type of operation is the monostable mode, illustrated in

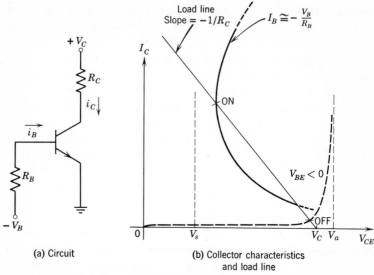

(a) Circuit   (b) Collector characteristics
                                        and load line

Fig. 3.23. Bistable operation of an avalanche mode transistor.

Fig. 3.24. The stable OFF state occurs with the emitter junction
reverse-biased. The dc load line, of slope $-1/R_C$ is chosen to have
no intersection with the avalanche-mode constant-reverse-base-
current characteristic curve. When the circuit is triggered into
the ON state by a pulse at either the base or collector, the collector
current increases abruptly along the dynamic load line of slope
$-1/R_L$ to the indicated point, which can be at a very high collector
current. This condition is not stable, however, and the collector current decays as the capacitor charges. When the capacitor reaches
a value at which the constant-base-current characteristic is
tangent to the dynamic load line (designated as I_T in Fig. 3.24b),
the system switches back to a low-current state.

The monostable avalanche-mode circuit is capable of producing
output pulses which combine very high currents and very fast
rise times. The high-speed capability results from the fact that the
internal feedback associated with the avalanche multiplication
can build up very rapidly. The maximum repetition rate of the
circuit is limited by the transistor dissipation in the metastable ON
state.

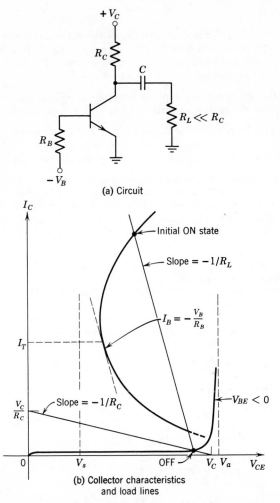

(a) Circuit

(b) Collector characteristics
and load lines

Fig. 3.24. A monostable avalanche-mode pulse generator.

PROBLEMS

P3.1 As an alternative to the calculation of the magnitude of the loop transmission of the circuit in Fig. 3.3a by calculating V'/V as in Fig. 3.3c, show that one could equally well inject a current I at point A and calculate the resulting current through $R_{B2} + (R_{in}||R_{B1})$.

P3.2 Calculate the magnitude of the loop transmission for the circuit in Fig. 3.3a by the method suggested in Fig. 3.3d, and check with Eq. 3.10.

P3.3 Repeat P3.2, except use the circuit in Fig. 3.4. Assume the α_0 generator is an independent generator $\alpha_0 I_1'$, and calculate the resulting current I_1 through $r_{\pi 1}/\beta_{01}$, and hence find the loop transmission I_1/I_1'.

P3.4 This problem is concerned with the circuit of Fig. 3.1. Note that a larger value of R_{C2} will cause the second transistor to be *saturated* when the first transistor is cut off. Assuming that $R_{C2} = 4$ k and all the other element values are unchanged, determine the complete static transfer characteristic which relates v_O and v_I. Make the same simplifying assumptions introduced in Sec. 3.1.1.

P3.5 The circuit shown in Fig. 3.25 can be made bistable if the resistors R_B are chosen properly.
  (a) Determine a suitable value for R_B and describe the two stable states concisely.
  (b) Sketch and label an incremental model of this bistable circuit for both transistors active, and calculate the incremental loop transmission.

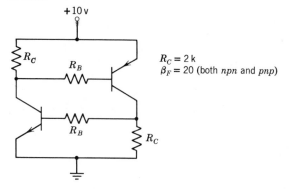

Fig. 3.25. A complementary bistable circuit.

P3.6 Determine the duration of the timed interval of the monostable multivibrator shown in Fig. 3.16a, i.e., verify Eq. 3.23.

P3.7 Consider the cross-coupled monostable circuit illustrated in Fig. 3.17a, in which T_2 is off and T_1 is on in the stable state. Compute, sketch, and dimension waveforms which describe the behavior of this circuit following a trigger pulse which causes a transition to the metastable state.

P3.8 This problem refers to the astable multivibrator circuit of Fig. 3.18a.

(a) With the capacitors removed, both transistors must be biased in the active region. What limitations does this constraint place on the relative values of the resistors in the circuit?

(b) Select an appropriate set of resistor values and supply voltages. Assume that $\beta_F = 50$.

(c) Using the element values chosen in (b), evaluate the incremental loop transmission with the coupling capacitors shorted. Assume that the transistor operating points are those which obtain when the capacitors are removed.

P3.9 (a) Draw the general y-parameter representation for two two-port networks connected in parallel (i.e., Fig. 3.10, MTC).

(b) Prove that, if the reverse transmission y_{ra} of the basic amplifier is negligible, a loop transmission

$$T = \frac{y_{rf}\,y_{fa}}{(Y_S + y_{ia} + y_{if})(y_{oa} + y_{of} + Y_L) - y_{ff}y_{rf}}$$

can be found either by direct calculation or by breaking the loop in a manner similar to that shown in Fig. 3.3c or d.

4

Boolean Algebra and Functional Blocks

4.0 INTRODUCTION

Since this book is primarily concerned with the application of semiconductors to digital circuits, no attempt will be made to present a complete and rigorous treatment of Boolean algebra. For many readers the material in this chapter will be in the nature of a review. However, because the notation and presentation of Boolean algebra, as applied to electronic circuits, differs somewhat from that encountered in a more formal course in Boolean algebra, it will be helpful to set forth the rules and relationships which will be used subsequently.

The algebra ordinarily used in engineering problems makes use of the entire field of numbers—including complex and transcendental numbers. For Boolean algebra only two values or states of a variable are permitted. Therefore, Boolean algebra is naturally suited for the description of circuits which operate in one or the other of two states and which are driven by and produce signals that fall within one or the other of two nonoverlapping ranges of values. We have seen numerous examples of such circuits in Chapters 2 and 3. In such cases Boolean algebra can be used to describe the logical functions of circuits succinctly, and to express the signal-processing properties of complex assemblies of switching circuits in a compact and unequivocal way. Consequently, Boolean algebra becomes a useful tool in the analysis and design of switching circuits.

The two values of a binary or Boolean variable are usually represented by the symbols **0** and **1**, although for specific applications other forms are used, such as "true" and "false" (referring to a statement), ON and OFF (referring to a switch), or "set" and "reset" (referring to a bistable circuit or device).

Because of the limited range of values which a variable may assume, the rules of Boolean algebra are quite different from those of ordinary algebra. A Boolean algebra may be defined in terms of three operations: *complementation*, *addition*, and *multiplication*. These will be described below.

In the material which follows, Boolean addition and multiplication will be represented symbolically by a bold face plus sign ($+$) and a small star ($*$) respectively. Also Boolean variables will be in boldface. This will distinguish the Boolean operations and symbols from arithmetic and algebraic operations, where the conventional symbols are used.

4.1 BASIC BOOLEAN RELATIONS

4.1.1 *Definitions*

A Boolean variable, x, has two possible values, **0** and **1**. By definition, these values are exclusive, that is

$$\text{if} \quad x \neq 1, \quad \text{then } x = 0$$
$$\text{if} \quad x \neq 0, \quad \text{then } x = 1$$

A Boolean function is determined when a relationship is given between two or more independent Boolean variables. Of course, all Boolean variables appearing in such a function must satisfy the restrictions stated above.

4.1.2 *Postulates*

The following postulates are adopted for the three basic operations of addition, multiplication, and complementation. Together, these postulates are sufficient to derive all Boolean relations.

Addition	*Multiplication*	*Complementation*
$0 + 0 = 0$	$0 * 0 = 0$	$0' = 1$
$0 + 1 = 1$	$1 * 0 = 0$	$1' = 0$
$1 + 0 = 1$	$0 * 1 = 0$	
$1 + 1 = 1$	$1 * 1 = 1$	

Although the prime symbol is used here to indicate the operation of complementation, the use of a bar is also common, as $\bar{x}$. The disadvantage of using the bar is the confusion which may occur when it is used in a very complex Boolean expression where successive and multiple complementation is to be indicated.

4.1.3 *Additional Relations*

There are certain relations easily derived from the above postulates which are useful in manipulating algebraic expressions of Boolean functions. (*Note.* When two variables are written next to one another, Boolean multiplication is to be understood, i.e., $xy = x * y$.)

	Addition	*Multiplication*
(1) *Unit and Zero Rules*	$0 + x = x$	$0 * x = 0$
	$1 + x = 1$	$1 * x = x$
(2) *Idempotence Laws*	$x + x = x$	$x * x = x$
(3) *Complementarity*	$x + x' = 1$	$x * x' = 0$
(4) *Involution*	$(x')' = x$	
(5) *Commutativity*	$x + y = y + x$	$xy = yx$
(6) *Associativity*	$x + (y + z) = (x + y) + z$	$x(yz) = (xy)z$
(7) *Distributivity*	$x + yz = (x + y)(x + z)$	$x(y + z) = xy + xz$
(8) *Absorption laws*	$x + xy = x$	
	$x(x + y) = x$	
	$x + x'y = x + y$	
(9) *DeMorgan's theorems*		

$$(x + y)' = x'y'$$
$$(xy)' = x' + y'$$

With regard to the distributive property in relation 7 above; the second relation states that, as in ordinary algebra, Boolean multiplication is distributive with respect to addition. The first relation shows that, *unlike* ordinary algebra, Boolean addition is distributive with respect to multiplication. That is, the left side directs us to form the product **yz** first, before adding it to **x**. The right side, however, directs us first to add **y** to **x**, and **z** to **x**, and then form the product of the results. A proof of this property will be given in a later section.

The absorption laws, relations 8, may be derived using the first distributive law above, along with variations of the relations which precede it.

4.1.4 *Use of DeMorgan's Theorems*

DeMorgan's theorems are extremely useful when it is necessary to form the complement of a Boolean function. In order to find the complement of a function which consists of several variables summed together, each uncomplemented variable is complemented while each complemented variable is uncomplemented. The plus signs are then replaced by stars. For example

$$(x + y' + z')' = x' * y * z$$

The same operation may be performed on an expression consisting of a sum of a number of product terms, thus:

$$(x'y + xy'z' + yz)' = (x'y)' * (xy'z')' * (yz)'$$
$$= (x + y') * (x' + y + z) * (y' + z')$$

DeMorgan's theorems are very important in dealing with complicated Boolean expressions. An expression which seems hopelessly complex is sometimes reduced to relatively simple proportions through the successive application of these theorems and the rules stated above.

DeMorgan's theorem also points out the duality aspect which is principal to all Boolean algebra. Each theorem or function has a *dual*, which may be found by complementing each side of the equality expressed by the theorem or function. Also, as will be shown later, this duality can be extended to circuits. It can be shown, using DeMorgan's theorem, that the entire algebra can be derived using only the **(+)** and **(')** operations, or conversely, using only the (∗) and (′) operations. This fact is frequently used in the design of practical digital circuits.

4.1.5 *Interpretation of Boolean Operations*

The operations just described may be applied to the real world in a meaningful fashion, as will be seen below.

Complement (′)

The complement is the negation or "not" of the statement represented by the function: i.e., if the variable **A** represents the state of a door and if $A = 1$ denotes that the door is open, $A' = 1$ means the door is *not* open.

Multiplication (∗)

Logical multiplication may be interpreted as the "necessary and" statement. Thus if the variables **A** and **B** represent the states of doors, and if either of these variables is 1 when the corresponding door is open, $A ∗ B$ is a variable which is 1 only when both doors **A** *and* **B** are open.

Sum (+)

The logical sum expresses the "inclusive or" statement. Thus, continuing the example above, $A + B = 1$ would mean that doors **A** *or* **B** are open *or both* are open.

Circle Sum (⊕)

The circle sum is not an independent operation as such; it can be expressed in terms of the other operations above. It arises so frequently, however, that it is sometimes considered to be an operation in itself in order to avoid the more lengthy expression. The circle sum is the "exclusive or." Thus $A ⊕ B = 1$ means door **A** *or* **B** but *not both* is open. We may expand this particular operation by using the rules above. The statement above may be expressed symbolically as:

$$A ⊕ B = (A + B)(AB)'$$
$$= (A + B)(A' + B') \quad \text{(DeMorgan's theorem)}$$
$$= AA' + AB' + BA' + BB'$$
$$= AB' + BA'$$

The complement of $A \oplus B$ is:

$$(A \oplus B)' = (AB' + BA')'$$
$$= (AB')'(BA')'$$
$$= (A' + B)(B' + A)$$
$$= A'B' + AA' + BB' + BA$$
$$= AB + A'B'$$

It is instructive to check these manipulative results by stating each side in "logical words" and noting that the equation makes sense.

4.2 TABLE OF COMBINATIONS

4.2.1 *Analysis of a Boolean Function*

An important concept in dealing with Boolean algebra is the table of combinations or, as it is commonly called, the "truth table." A table of combinations is simply a complete listing (analysis) of all possible values for the variables in a Boolean function. Since each variable may have either of two values, a Boolean function of n variables must have 2^n listings in the table in order to cover all possible combinations. Once a table of this sort is made, additional columns are made to contain various combinations of these variables or their primes (complements) and finally the value of the entire function itself. It becomes obvious, therefore, that since *all* possible states have been tabulated, use of a table of combinations to confirm a Boolean function constitutes *proof by perfect induction*.

A table of combinations is often useful for checking certain expressions when in doubt about their accuracy. Conversely, we may go from a table of combinations to a Boolean expression (synthesis) and thence to a circuit which will realize the relationships expressed in the table.

As an example, let us tabulate the function $x + yz = (x + y)(x + z)$ (Table 4.1). This is the distributive law for addition [Sec. 4.1.3]. Since the results are so different from ordinary algebra, the table provides not only convincing proof of the property but also some feeling as to *why* it makes "Boolean sense."

TABLE 4.1

Table of combinations for $x + yz = (x + y)(x + z)$

Values for Variables			Left Side of Equation		Right Side of Equation		
x	y	z	yz	$(x + yz)$	$x + y$	$x + z$	$(x + y)(x + z)$
0	0	0	0	0	0	0	0
0	0	1	0	0	0	1	0
0	1	0	0	0	1	0	0
0	1	1	1	1	1	1	1
1	0	0	0	1	1	1	1
1	0	1	0	1	1	1	1
1	1	0	0	1	1	1	1
1	1	1	1	1	1	1	1

Since the values of both sides of the relation $x + yz = (x + y)(x + z)$ agree for every possible combination of values which the variables may have, the relation is verified.

As another example, let us form the tables of combinations for the circle sum and its complement as derived in Sec. 4.1.5.

$$A \oplus B = AB' + A'B'$$
$$(A \oplus B)' = AB + A'B'$$

The results are shown in Tables 4.2 and 4.3.

TABLE 4.2

Table of combinations for $A \oplus B = AB' + A'B$

A	B	A'	B'	AB'	A'B	$AB' + A'B = A \oplus B$
0	0	1	1	0	0	0
0	1	1	0	0	1	1
1	0	0	1	1	0	1
1	1	0	0	0	0	0

TABLE 4.3

Table of combinations for $(A \oplus B)' = AB + A'B'$

A	B	A'	B'	AB	A'B'	$AB + A'B' = (A \oplus B)'$
0	0	1	1	0	1	1
0	1	1	0	0	0	0
1	0	0	1	0	0	0
1	1	0	0	1	0	1

It can now be seen why the circle sum is the *exclusive or*, since the function is **1** only when **A** or **B** is **1** but not when both **A** and **B** are **1**.

In a similar manner, we may provide proofs for any Boolean expression. This method, although certainly providing convincing proof of the "truth" of a relation, can become very cumbersome when applied to a function with a great many variables. In these cases it is usually more efficient to carry out algebraic manipulations directly, using the rules given above.

4.2.2 *Synthesis of a Boolean Function*

In Sec. 4.2.1 it was shown how a Boolean function may be analyzed by writing a table of combinations which includes all possible combinations of values of its variables. The inverse operation, viz., the synthesis of a Boolean function from a given table of combinations of the values of its variables, is an extremely useful operation. As before, if n is the number of variables in the Boolean function, the table must contain 2^n entries. The procedure is first to write a listing of all possible states for the variables, preferably as a binary sequence, and then in a parallel column, a listing of the value of the desired function for each position in the table. The function may then be synthesized directly by writing it as the sum of all terms (each expressed as the Boolean product of *all* the independent variables) where the function has a value of **1**. That is, each row of the table for which the function has the value **1** contributes a term to the sum. Alternatively, we may write the sum of the complements of all the terms where the function has a value of **0**. The resulting Boolean function can then be simplified by algebraic manipulation.

As an example of the synthesis technique, consider a Boolean function, **F(x, y)**, which has the combinations given in Table 4.4.

TABLE 4.4

Table of combinations for F(x, y)

x	y	F(x, y)
0	0	1
0	1	1
1	0	0
1	1	1

Writing the sum of the Boolean product of **x** and **y** for each row in the table for which $F(x, y) = 1$, we get

$$F(x, y) = x'y' + x'y + xy$$

Using the relations previously given, this expression can be reduced.

$$F(x, y) = x'(y' + y) + xy$$
$$= x' + xy$$
$$= (x' + x)(x' + y)$$
$$F(x, y) = x' + y$$

Alternatively, we may synthesize the function by using the term where the function is zero.

$$F(x, y) = (xy')'$$
$$= x' + y \qquad \text{(DeMorgan's theorem)}$$

Any complex function may be similarly synthesized.

Sometimes we discover regularities in the table which permit factoring the terms by inspection thus allowing simpler expressions to be written. In addition, minimization techniques have been developed for systematically reducing such a table and/or set of terms to a minimum form—a kind of "least common denominator" approach. Some of these techniques may be found in the listed references.

4.3 BASIC FUNCTIONS AND BUILDING BLOCKS

Although there may be a great many logic functions used in the algebraic description of a digital system, they all employ only *three* basic functional operations. These operations are complementation ($'$), addition ($+$), and multiplication ($*$). It is possible to express any Boolean function in terms of either the addition and complementation operations alone or in terms of the multiplication and complementation operations alone. Nevertheless, it is convenient in a digital system to have the capability of mechanization of all three operations.

As we have seen in Chapter 2, a simple transistor circuit, the inverter, can be used to produce the algebraic operation of complementation. We shall find in Chapters 5 and 6 that other circuits involving transistors and diodes can be used to mechanize the operations of addition and multiplication. Therefore, it is desirable to introduce a block diagram representation for these basic functional operations, and for their combinations in Boolean functions. Such a graphical representation of algebraic relationships is useful in both the analysis and synthesis of digital systems. We now consider simple block-diagram representations for basic algebraic operations. Circuit realizations of these functional relationships are discussed in Chapters 5, 6, and 7.

4.3.1 *Inversion*

The inverter performs the simplest algebraic operation. Figure 4.1 shows the table of combinations and block-diagram representation of an inverter. There is a single input corresponding to a Boolean variable **x**, and an output which is the Boolean function, $y = x'$. The operation of inversion is frequently obtained as a "by-product" of other operations, as will be seen below.

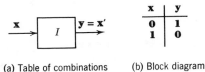

(a) Table of combinations   (b) Block diagram

Fig. 4.1. The inverter, which performs the logical operation of complementation.

4.3.2 *AND Gate*

The AND gate performs the Boolean multiplication (∗) operation (Sec. 4.1.5) between variables. This circuit is called an *AND gate*, because the inputs perform a *gating* role in determining the output. That is, the output is in the **1** state only when all the inputs simultaneously are in the **1** state. If any one of them is in the **0** state, the output is also in the **0** state. A block diagram symbol and table of combinations for a three-input AND gate are shown in Fig. 4.2.

4.3.3 *NAND Gate*

If the AND gate, described above, includes as a part of its circuitry an output inverter, the circuit is called a NAND gate

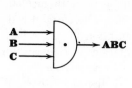

Inputs			Output
A	**B**	**C**	**ABC**
0	0	0	0
0	0	1	0
0	1	0	0
0	1	1	0
1	0	0	0
1	0	1	0
1	1	0	0
1	1	1	1

(a) Block–diagram symbol   (b) Table of combinations

Fig. 4.2. Three-input AND gate block symbol and its table of combinations.

(see Fig. 4.3). If the inputs are the Boolean variables **A**, **B**, and **C**, the output will be **(ABC)′**. Expanding this by DeMorgan's theorem we get

$$(\mathbf{ABC})' = \mathbf{A}' + \mathbf{B}' + \mathbf{C}'$$

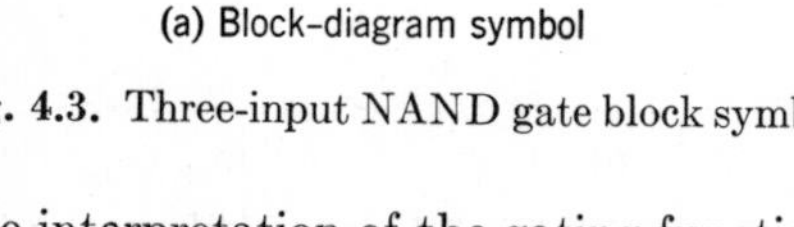

Inputs			Output
A	**B**	**C**	**(ABC)′**
0	0	0	1
0	0	1	1
0	1	0	1
0	1	1	1
1	0	0	1
1	0	1	1
1	1	0	1
1	1	1	0

(a) Block–diagram symbol   (b) Table of combinations

Fig. 4.3. Three-input NAND gate block symbol and its table of combinations.

The interpretation of the gating function shown here is that if any one of the variables **A**, **B**, or **C** is in the **0** state, the output will be in the **1** state. Conversely, only if all the input variables are in the **1** state will the output be in the **0** state. The table in Fig. 4.3 indicates this relationship.

4.3.4 *OR Gate*

The OR gate performs the Boolean operation of addition **(+)** between variables. A block-diagram symbol for a 3-input OR gate is shown in Fig. 4.4, together with its table of combinations. The gating function is understood by noting that the output has a

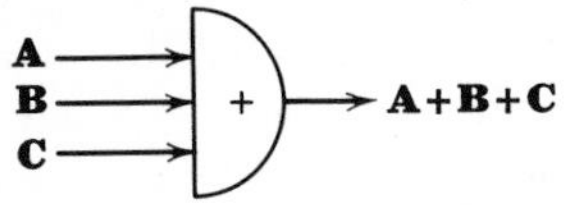

Inputs			Output
A	**B**	**C**	**A+B+C**
0	0	0	0
0	0	1	1
0	1	0	1
0	1	1	1
1	0	0	1
1	0	1	1
1	1	0	1
1	1	1	1

(a) Block–diagram symbol

(b) Table of combinations

Fig. 4.4. Three-input OR gate block symbol and its table of combinations.

1 state when any one or more of the input variables are in the 1 state. Conversely, only when *all* the input variables are in the 0 state will the output also be in the 0 state.

4.3.5 *NOR Gate*

If the OR gate described above has an inverter associated with its output, the output function is inverted and the circuit is known as a NOR gate (see Fig. 4.5). If the input variables are **A**, **B**, and **C**, the output will be $(A + B + C)'$.

The gating function shown here indicates that if any input variable is in the 1 state the output will be in the 0 state. Conversely, *all* inputs must be in the 0 state for the output to be in the 1 state. The table in Fig. 4.5 shows this relation.

4.3.6 *Fan-In and Fan-Out in Logic Blocks*

We shall see in Chapters 5 and 6 that the circuits used to imple-

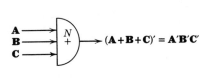

Inputs			Output
A	**B**	**C**	**(A+B+C)'**
0	0	0	1
0	0	1	0
0	1	0	0
0	1	1	0
1	0	0	0
1	0	1	0
1	1	0	0
1	1	1	0

(a) Block–diagram symbol

(b) Table of combinations

Fig. 4.5. Three-input NOR gate block symbol and its table of combinations.

ment basic logic functions invariably have limited capabilities with respect to the number of inputs and outputs that can be accommodated. The maximum number of independent input variables that can be used with a logic block is called the maximum *fan-in*. For example, if a certain circuit realization of an *AND* gate, shown in block-diagram form in Fig. 4.2, is limited to five inputs, the gate is said to have a fan-in of five.

The number of logic blocks that can be driven by a given block is also limited by circuit considerations. This limitation is often set by the maximum output-current capability of a transistor switch. The maximum number of logic blocks that can be driven by another block is called the maximum *fan-out*.

While fan-in and fan-out limitations are inseparable from the details of the circuit realization used, it is important to keep these limitations in mind when constructing logic block diagrams; no logic block must be employed in a manner which would require more inputs or outputs than the circuit can accommodate.

4.3.7 *Signal Representation and Logical Function*

When an electronic circuit is used to mechanize or realize a logical operation it is necessary to assign ranges of a signal or machine variable to correspond to the two states of the associated binary variable. For example, if binary variables are represented in a digital system by voltage levels, as discussed in Chapter 1, specific nonoverlapping voltage ranges must be assigned to the two values of the binary variable.

In the foregoing discussion of basic logic gates nothing has been said about the relationship between physical variables and Boolean variables. We now define several common forms of signal representation and show that the logical function of a gate may change entirely when the signal representation changes. For illustrative purposes we assume that Boolean variables are represented by *voltage levels*; exactly analogous considerations apply for other choices of physical variables.

We define four alternative forms of voltage representation.

(1) *Positive representation.* The voltage range assigned to the **1** state is more *positive* than the range assigned to the **0** state.

(2) *Negative representation.* The voltage range assigned to the **1** state is more *negative* than the range assigned to the **0** state.

(3) *Bipolar representation.* A special case of *positive* representation in which the voltage ranges have equal magnitudes but opposite polarity, e.g., $+5$ to $+6$ volts and -5 to -6 volts.

(4) *Inverted representation.* A special case of negative representation in which the voltage ranges have equal magnitude but opposite polarity.

An important principle follows from a consideration of these various forms of voltage representation. *A gate which performs the Boolean AND operation for positive representation will perform the Boolean OR operation when negative representation is used*, and vice versa. Similarly, a gate which performs the Boolean NAND operation for positive representation will perform the Boolean NOR operation when negative representation is used, and vice versa. The demonstration of this principle is left as a problem (P4.7). The particular choice of voltage representation thus affects the form of logic equations which must be written for a particular kind of gate.

4.4 BOOLEAN VARIABLES AND BINARY NUMBERS

Since the Boolean variable has only two discrete values, the variable may be used to represent ordinary arithmetic operations between binary numbers in a particularly simple fashion.

We have seen that it is important to distinguish carefully between the "addition" and "multiplication" *operations* in Boolean algebra and those of ordinary (binary) arithmetic. Similarly, it is important to distinguish between the values **0** and **1** which a Boolean function may have and the counting symbols 0 and 1 used in the binary numbering system. To aid in this distinction values of a Boolean variable have been set in boldface. Unfortunately, such a convention is not used throughout the literature. Although the issue may seem confusing at first, a little thought will usually show which of the two is being considered at any particular stage of the problem.

4.5 SYNTHESIS OF A BOOLEAN FUNCTION FROM A SET OF BINARY NUMBERS

In the practical design of digital systems, it is usual to perform various arithmetical operations between binary numbers. It becomes necessary to derive Boolean functions to represent these operations, since the computing elements are usually defined in terms of Boolean *operations*. In order to illustrate this technique, consider the operation of adding two binary numbers together. The process is summarized here for convenience.

Consider two binary numbers A and B, together with a carry C and a sum S. We will use a subscript as a positional notation referring to the power of 2. Thus A_0 is the coefficient (1 or 0) associated with the term 2_0, etc. Accordingly a binary number may be written as

$$A = \sum_{j=0}^{i} A_j 2^j$$

The addition of two binary numbers A and B is accomplished as follows

$$\begin{array}{l} A = A_i 2^i + A_{i-1} 2^{i-1} + \cdots A_1 2^1 + A_0 2^0 \\ B = B_i 2^i + B_{i-1} 2^{i-1} + \cdots B_1 2^1 + B_0 2^0 \\ \underline{C = C_i 2^i + C_{i-1} 2^{i-1} + \cdots C_1 2^1} \\ S = S_i 2^i + S_{i-1} 2^{i-1} + \cdots S_1 2^1 + S_0 2^0 \end{array} \quad (C_0 \equiv 0)$$

The carry is defined in the usual sense. A_0 and B_0 are the least significant bits of the numbers A and B. If $A_0 = 1$ and $B_0 = 1$, the sum is 0 with a carry, hence $C_1 = 1$ and must be added to the sum of A_1 and B_1, etc. We shall now form a table of binary values (Table 4.5) for the three terms A_1, B_1, and C_1 together with the sum and next carry bit.

TABLE 4.5

Table of binary values for a single-stage binary adder

Binary Values			Sum	Carry to Next Bit
A_1	B_1	C_1	S_1	C_2
0	0	0	0	0
0	0	1	1	0
0	1	0	1	0
0	1	1	0	1
1	0	0	1	0
1	0	1	0	1
1	1	0	0	1
1	1	1	1	1

Note that the entries in this table are *binary numbers*. The table illustrates the operation of *binary addition*.

Now let us shift our thinking about the symbols above and, instead, consider A_1, B_1, and C_1 in Table 4.5 as Boolean variables. Similarly, consider S_1 and C_2 as *Boolean functions of these three variables*. Thus, Table 4.5 can now be regarded as a table of combinations which expresses these Boolean functions. Strictly speaking, we should now construct a table, identical to Table 4.5 except with all symbols in boldface, to indicate that we are now speaking of Boolean operations, however we shall merely keep this fact in mind in the discussion which follows. With these considerations in mind, we may write Boolean expressions for S_1 and C_2 as was done in Sec. 4.2.2. Each expression will contain a term in the three independent variables for each row in the table for which the function has the value 1.

Although the expressions obtained by the above method may be simplified by use of the basic Boolean rules given at the beginning of the chapter, it is possible to bypass some of the manipulations by observing certain regularities in the table. The following derivation will show the nature of this approach.

Note that in the column headed *Sum*, S_1 has the value of 1 for four combinations of values of the variables A_1, B_1, and C_1. Since this is an "or" statement or logical sum idea, S_1 may be written down directly.

$$S_1 = A_1'B_1'C_1 + A_1'B_1C_1' + A_1B_1'C_1' + A_1B_1C_1$$
$$= C_1(A_1B_1 + A_1'B_1') + C_1'(A_1B_1' + A_1'B_1)$$

The expressions in the parentheses will be recognized as $(A_1 \oplus B_1)'$ and $(A_1 + B_1)$ respectively, so the sum reduces to

$$S_1 = C_1(A_1 \oplus B_1)' + C_1'(A_1 \oplus B_1)$$

The expression for the carry to the next bit is

$$C_2 = A_1'B_1C_1 + A_1B_1'C_1 + A_1B_1C_1' + A_1B_1C_1$$
$$= (A_1'B_1 + A_1B_1')C_1 + A_1B_1(C_1 + C_1')$$
$$= (A_1'B_1 + A_1B_1')C_1 + A_1B_1$$
$$= (A_1 \oplus B_1)C_1 + A_1B_1$$

As an illustration of simplifying operations, let us take the very first expression above for C_2 and add the last term, $A_1B_1C_1$, two more times. From the idempotence law for addition, it is apparent that this does not change the function. If the terms are now regrouped in pairs, we have the different result,

$$C_2 = (A_1 + B_1)C_1 + A_1B_1$$

which is simpler than the former expression.

For the special case of the least significant bit, $C_0 = 0$ and $C_0' = 1$ at all times, since there never can be a carry. The first sum and carry therefore become

$$S_0 = A_0 \oplus B_0 = A_0B_0' + A_0'B_0$$

and

$$C_1 = A_0B_0$$

As an example of the use of block diagrams to represent Boolean functions and as a first step in the realization of a prescribed logical operation, we illustrate in Fig. 4.6 one possible block diagram for the carry C_2 expression above. We *assume* that only AND and OR gates are available. Consequently, as necessary, complements of variables must be generated with inverters. Figure 4.6 shows that the synthesis technique proceeds in an orderly fashion. The innermost product terms are formed in AND gates, whose outputs are summed in an OR gate. Similarly, the other terms are formed and combined until the entire function is generated.

If the function used in this example is expressed in a different algebraic form, a different logic form may be realized. In general,

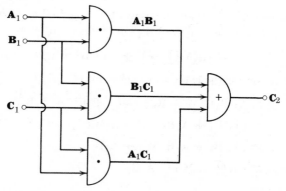

Fig. 4.6. Block diagram realization of C_2 expression.

there are many different logic forms which can realize the same Boolean function. An important task of the logic designer is to select the form which is best suited to the kind of circuits used.

REFERENCES

4.1 Bartee, T. C., Lebow, I., and Reed, I. S., *Theory and Design of Digital Machines*, McGraw-Hill, New York, 1962.

4.2 Hurley, R. B., *Transistor Logic Circuits*, John Wiley & Sons, Inc., New York, 1961.

4.3 Grabbe, E. M., Ramo, S., and Wooldridge, D. E., *Handbook of Automation Computation and Control*, Vol. 2, John Wiley & Sons, Inc., New York, 1959.

4.4 Caldwell, S. H., *Switching Circuits and Logical Design*, John Wiley and Sons, Inc., New York, 1958.

PROBLEMS

P4.1 There are 16 different functions of 2 variables, x and y. Using a table of combinations of x and y, complete the tabulation of all 16 functions and express each as a Boolean function (e.g., the previously derived circle sum $\oplus$ and its complement are two of the functions).

P4.2 Show that:

$$xyz + xyz' + xy'z + xy'z' + x'yz = x + yz.$$

P4.3 Show that:

$$abcd + abcd' + a'bcd' + a'bc'd' + a'b'cd'$$
$$+ a'b'c'd' = abc + a'd'.$$

P4.4 Simplify:

(*a*) $a(ab + c) + a'(c' + b)$
(*b*) $(a + b + c')d + (a' + b)c$
(*c*) $(a + b)'c + (ac)' + ab$
(*d*) $[(a + b + c)' + (ab + ac)']'$

P4.5 Prove:

$$(A_1 \oplus B_1)C_1 + A_1B_1 = (A_1 + B_1)C_1 + A_1B_1$$

P4.6 Prove the distributive law for addition with respect to multiplication without using a truth table. Use the other relationships of Sec. 4.1.

P4.7 Show that the Boolean operations performed by AND and OR gates (positive representation) are interchanged when negative representation is used.

P4.8 Show that the Boolean operations performed by NAND and NOR gates (positive representation) are interchanged when negative representation is used.

P4.9 Draw the block diagram to realize the function

$$F = [(ABC' + B'D)' + BC + B'E]G$$

using NAND and NOR gates only.

P4.10 Since a NAND gate or a NOR gate becomes an inverter if only one input is used, draw the block diagram for the above function using only NAND gates.

5

Passive Logic Circuits

5.0 INTRODUCTION

There are a number of different circuit techniques which have been used to implement Boolean functions and operations. These techniques may be placed into two somewhat arbitrary categories which we will term *active* and *passive* logic circuits. The various logic circuit techniques have been given names which more or less describe the particular circuit configuration. Some of the more common configurations are listed below.

Active Logic Circuits

Resistor-Transistor Logic	RTL
Diode-Transistor Logic	DTL
Direct-Coupled-Transistor Logic	DCTL
Current-Mode Logic	CML
Transistor-Transistor Logic	TTL

Passive Logic Circuits

Continuity Logic	CL
Resistor Logic	RL
Diode Logic	DL

This chapter takes up the matter of RL and DL circuits—primarily from a Boolean operational point of view. The final section will be devoted to a more detailed analysis of worst-case conditions in diode logic. Active circuits will be treated in Chapters 6 and 7.

5.1 RESISTOR LOGIC (RL)

5.1.1 *Linear Addition of Binary Signals*

Let us consider the resistive network in Fig. 5.1 to see whether it will perform Boolean operations on binary signals. We shall let 0 volts represent the Boolean "0" and +1 volts represent the Boolean "1." (For convenience we shall use positive representation throughout this chapter). It is clear that the output voltage will bear a linear relationship to the input voltages. In particular, if the input voltages have only the two values of 0 and +1 volt, the

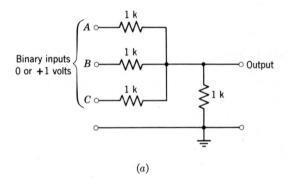

(a)

Inputs in Volts			Output in Volts
A	B	C	
0	0	0	0
0	0	1	0.25
0	1	0	0.25
0	1	1	0.5
1	0	0	0.25
1	0	1	0.5
1	1	0	0.5
1	1	1	0.75

(b)

Fig. 5.1. The linear addition of three binary signals (0 or +1 v).

output will have a value of 0, 0.25, 0.5, or 0.75 volt, depending on whether 0, 1, 2, or 3 of the inputs are at the 1-volt level. This relationship is shown in the table of Fig. 5.1. Clearly, the *representation* has changed between input and output.

5.1.2 *Binary Detection and Level Restoration*

Although we have demonstrated the linear addition of binary signals, the output is no longer in a binary form since four different voltage levels are obtained. In order to convert this output to binary form, an ideal Schmitt trigger (see Secs. 3.1 and 3.2) will be used as a detector and level restorer. Figure 5.2a shows the circuit symbol for the Schmitt trigger, the circuit details are not important for this discussion. It is assumed that for any input voltage *above* a *critical voltage*, the output is +1 volt (Boolean "**1**"), while for any input voltage *below* this critical voltage the output is 0 volts (Boolean "**0**"). The adjustable bias allows the critical voltage to be set as desired. Thus, level restoration is accomplished for any variation of input level around the critical voltage. Actually, the Schmitt trigger acts to convert from a level representation at the input to a state representation (its own state) internally, and

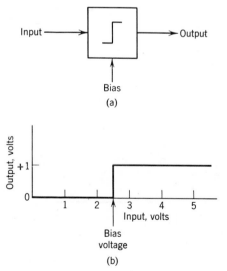

(a)

(b)

Fig 5.2. Ideal Schmitt trigger. (*a*) Circuit symbol. (*b*) Voltage transfer characteristics.

finally back to a level representation again at the output. The result is a considerable broadening of the permitted input "levels."

For clarity of exposition, the bias voltage is assumed to be identical in sign and magnitude to the critical voltage. Clearly, this is simply a matter of convention and scaling within the circuit. Figure 5.2b shows the resulting voltage transfer characteristic of this detector.

5.1.3 *OR Gate*

Figure 5.3 shows an OR gate using resistor logic. The bias voltage of the detector has been adjusted to 0.12 volt so that for an input above this value the output will be +1 volt (Boolean "1").

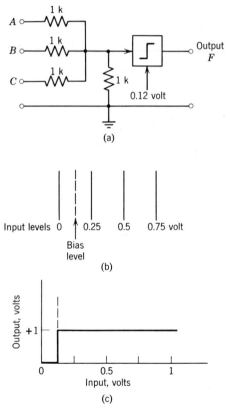

Fig. 5.3. OR gate using Resistor Logic. $\mathbf{F} = \mathbf{A} + \mathbf{B} + \mathbf{C}$. (*a*) Circuit arrangement. (*b*) Bias setting of Schmitt trigger. (*c*) Voltage transfer function of Schmitt trigger.

It is clear that for this bias setting, when any one or more of the inputs A, B, and C are at $+1$ volt, the output will be $+1$ volt, so that in terms of Boolean variables* we have $\mathbf{F} = \mathbf{A} + \mathbf{B} + \mathbf{C}$. Hence, we have an OR gate.

5.1.4 *AND Gate*

Figure 5.4 shows an AND gate using resistor logic. The bias voltage of the detector has been adjusted to 0.62 volt so that the output becomes $+1$ volt (Boolean "**1**") only when all three inputs

* In this and subsequent chapters we often indicate a node-to-ground voltage by a letter, and the Boolean variable that voltage represents by the same letter set in boldface type.

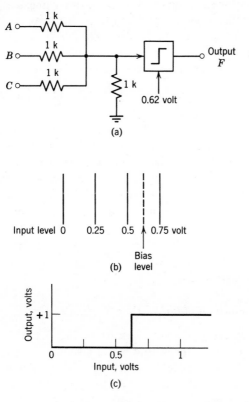

(a)

(b)

(c)

Fig. 5.4. AND gate using Resistor Logic. $\mathbf{F} = \mathbf{ABC}$. (*a*) Circuit arrangement. (*b*) Bias setting of Schmitt trigger. (*c*) Voltage transfer function of Schmitt trigger.

A, B, and C are simultaneously at $+1$ volt; hence the output in terms of Boolean variables is $F = ABC$, which is the AND function.

5.1.5 *Limitations of Resistor Logic*

The idealized examples just given are not too practical for the majority of digital logic requirements. Some difficulties associated with resistor logic are listed below.

(1) Interaction between input signals will occur because of the summing resistor which becomes a common coupling device.

(2) Since a detector is required at the output of each gate circuit, the amount of circuitry can become rather extensive.

(3) Significant gain is required to reconstitute the defined voltage representation for the Boolean variables.

(4) The bias level of each detector must be individually set so as to select the appropriate voltage level for each gate.

Because of these difficulties, the linear addition of binary signals is not widely used. It should be noted, however, that there are certain specialized applications where resistor logic can be quite useful. For example, they can be used to sense when the number of "one" inputs are less than or greater than some number, m. By setting the bias level of the detector, any m value may be chosen (see Problem P5.1). By using several circuits, together with inverters, it is possible to sense the occurrence of some exact number, n (see Problem P5.3). In this last application, however, it is usually easier to use a diode matrix, as will be shown in Sec. 5.2.5.

5.2 DIODE LOGIC (DL)

5.2.1 *Nonlinear Addition of Binary Signals*

If we replace the input resistors in Fig. 5.1 with a nonlinear resistance element, the output signal discrimination is made much easier. A diode is a highly nonlinear device, having an off-to-on current ratio often greater than 10^6. This property allows gate circuits to be designed with many inputs, while at the same time avoiding both the interaction between input signals and the wide range in output signal levels which are typical in resistor logic.

To compare the linear and nonlinear addition of binary signals, let us replace the input resistors of Fig. 5.1 with diodes as shown in Fig. 5.5a. For this example, we shall consider the diode as an *ideal switch*, i.e., when forward-biased its resistance and voltage drop are zero, and when reverse-biased the diode is an open circuit. As before, input signals of 0 and +1 volt represent the Boolean values of **0** and **1** respectively.

It is easily seen that the output is 1 volt when one or more of the inputs is 1 volt, and is 0 volts only when all the inputs are also 0 volts. Thus, the circuit performs the Boolean operation of addition (**+**) without the necessity of a voltage-level discriminator. It is seen that by using nonlinear addition of binary signals, it becomes particularly easy to construct Boolean logic circuits which have a *direct* binary output.

5.2.2 *Diode AND Gate*

Since the forward voltage drop of a silicon diode may range from 0.5 to 1.0 volt, the circuit just described is not very practical when

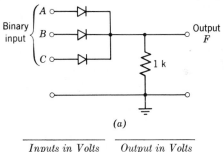

(a)

Inputs in Volts			Output in Volts
A	B	C	
0	0	0	0
0	0	1	1
0	1	0	1
0	1	1	1
1	0	0	1
1	0	1	1
1	1	0	1
1	1	1	1

(b)

Fig. 5.5. The *nonlinear* addition of binary signals which implements the Boolean OR operation, $\mathbf{F = A + B + C}$ (positive representation). In the voltage table, the diode is treated as an ideal switch.

used with such a low logic voltage. A more practical circuit is shown in Fig. 5.6. Here $+5$ volts represents a Boolean "1" and -5 volts represent a Boolean "0." The "summing" resistor is returned to $+30$ volts to provide unambiguous switching and relatively fast charging of circuit capacitances. Note that in the table of output voltages (Fig. 5.6d) we have assumed a 0.5 volt forward drop in the diodes. Although the output voltage levels do not coincide exactly with those of the input signals, the "forbidden" zone between the "0" level and the "1" level is still very wide and unambiguous.

The output of this AND gate must by necessity follow the *most negative* of the input signals, diodes having *less negative* input

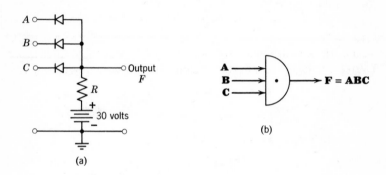

(a)

(b)

Inputs			Output		Inputs (Volts)			Output (Volts)
A	**B**	**C**	**F**		A	B	C	F
0	0	0	0		-5	-5	-5	-4.5
0	0	1	0		-5	-5	$+5$	-4.5
0	1	0	0		-5	$+5$	-5	-4.5
0	1	1	0		-5	$+5$	$+5$	-4.5
1	0	0	0		$+5$	-5	-5	-4.5
1	0	1	0		$+5$	-5	$+5$	-4.5
1	1	0	0		$+5$	$+5$	-5	-4.5
1	1	1	1		$+5$	$+5$	$+5$	$+5.5$

(c)

(d)

Fig. 5.6. Diode AND gate (positive representation). Tables of combinations are shown in (c) and (d). The forward voltage drop of the diode is taken as 0.5 volt.

signals becoming reverse-biased. Note that to preserve logic levels in DL circuits, *at least one diode must always be conducting.*

5.2.3 *Diode OR Gate*

Figure 5.7 shows a diode OR gate. Here the diodes have been reversed in direction and the "summing" resistor has been returned to −30 volts. Again, note that the output voltages differ from the input signal voltage representation for the Boolean variable. We can see that the output of this OR gate will always follow the *most positive* of the input signals, diodes having *less positive* input signals becoming reverse-biased.

5.2.4 *Multilevel Diode Gates*

The two forms of diode gates just described may be combined to generate more complicated functions. The output of one gate may

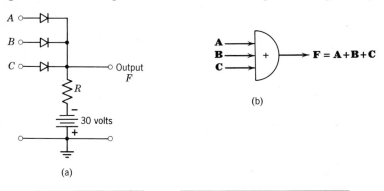

(b)

(a)

Inputs			Output		Inputs (Volts)			Output (Volts)
A	**B**	**C**	**F**		*A*	*B*	*C*	*F*
0	0	0	0		−5	−5	−5	−5.5
0	0	1	1		−5	−5	+5	+4.5
0	1	0	1		−5	+5	−5	+4.5
0	1	1	1		−5	+5	+5	+4.5
1	0	0	1		+5	−5	−5	+4.5
1	0	1	1		+5	−5	+5	+4.5
1	1	0	1		+5	+5	−5	+4.5
1	1	1	1		+5	+5	+5	+4.5

(c) (d)

Fig. 5.7. Diode OR gate (positive representation). Tables of combinations are shown in (*c*) and (*d*). The forward voltage drop of the diode is taken as 0.5 volt.

thus become the input of one or more other gates. Because of the forward drop in the diodes, the voltage levels may tend to depart more and more from the original input signal levels as additional gate circuits are traversed. Eventually it is necessary to introduce a circuit to restore the levels. This circuit may be a flip-flop, an inverter, or a buffer whose output is clamped at the two required voltage levels.

Figure 5.8 shows a simple example of two-level gating. The exclusive OR ($\oplus$) function is generated by two AND gates whose outputs are added together in an OR gate. The resulting function is $F = A \oplus B = AB' + A'B.$

The result of passing through first a diode AND gate and then a diode OR gate is that the original logic levels tend to be recovered. This is because the forward diode voltage drops cancel out approximately. If two successive AND gates are used, the loss in level will be double that indicated in the table of Fig. 5.6. The same is true for two OR gates. Hence, it is usually advisable to form complicated gating functions by using successive AND and OR gates.

5.2.5 *Diode Matrices* (*Decoder Networks*)

The term *diode matrix* has come to mean a diode network with inputs driven by voltage levels derived from an n-stage counter or register.* The matrix has up to 2^n output lines, each corresponding to a separate state of the driving counter or register. In actuality the diode matrix is nothing more than a large collection of gate circuits, all driven from the same source(s).

Diode matrices are widely used as address selection circuits because each output may represent a separate address in a memory. Diode matrices are also sometimes called *decoder networks* inasmuch as they decode the binary representation of a number contained in the input register into a signal on an output line which is identified with that number only.

A simple 8-output matrix is shown in Fig. 5.9. This particular form is often called a rectangular matrix from its appearance. Frequently there is redundancy in this direct approach to a decoding network. Judicious use of Boolean relationships, especially De-Morgan's Theorem, will usually lead to a simpler form. However,

---

* A counter or register consists of an arrangement of memory elements (e.g., bistable multivibrators) whose output represents a binary number.

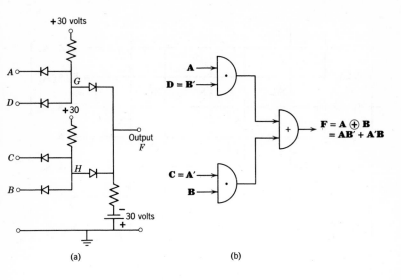

(a)　　　　　　　　　　　　　　　　(b)

Boolean Inputs				Output
A	**A′**	**B**	**B′**	**F**
0	1	0	1	0
0	1	1	0	1
1	0	0	1	1
1	0	1	0	0

(*c*)

Input Voltages				Outputs of AND Gates		Output of OR Gate
A	*B*	*C*	*D*	*G*	*H*	*F*
−5	+5	−5	+5	−4.5	−4.5	−5
−5	+5	+5	−5	−4.5	+5.5	+5
+5	−5	−5	+5	+5.5	−4.5	+5
+5	−5	+5	−5	−4.5	−4.5	−5

(*d*)

Fig. 5.8. Example of multilevel diode gating. The Exclusive OR **+** function has been generated. Note in table (*d*) that there has been a "restoration" of logic levels as a result of the signals passing first through the AND gates and then through the OR gates.

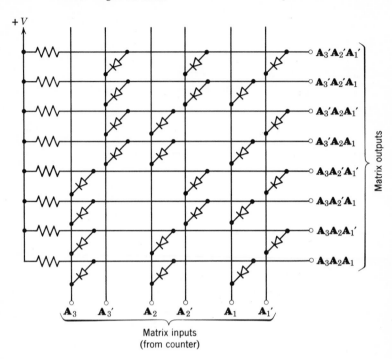

Matrix inputs
(from counter)

Fig. 5.9. Rectangular diode matrix.

it is very easy to implement a complicated Boolean function using
the matrix form and, because of this, it has been widely used.

5.2.6 *Limitations of Diode Logic*

One of the limitations of diode logic (already alluded to) arises
from diode forward voltage drop. There is an appreciable voltage
drop across a diode when it is conducting, and this voltage drop is
a function of temperature, as can be seen from Figs. 5.10 and 5.11.
(Compare these diode curves with those for the transistor junction
voltage V_{EB} as a function of temperature, Fig. 1.5b.) In addition,
the diodes used in a given circuit will not have identical $V-I$
characteristics. These variable voltage drops will cause undesired
spreading of the gate output voltage levels.

Reverse saturation currents can also adversely affect the behavior
of diode gates by limiting the number of diodes which can be used
in a single gate. A typical plot of saturation current versus tempera-

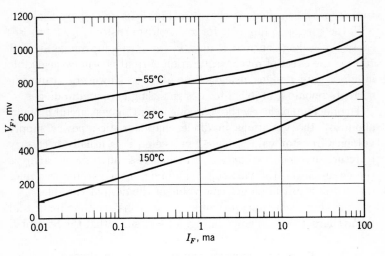

Fig. 5.10. Forward voltage vs. current for a planar, epitaxial, silicon diode.

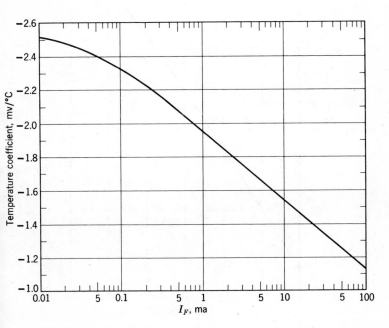

Fig. 5.11. Temperature coefficient $(\partial V_F/\partial T)|I_F$ vs. I_F for a silicon diode.

ture for a silicon diode is shown in Fig. 5.12. (Compare this plot with the corresponding plot for a silicon transistor, Fig. 1.4b.) Because the leakage current is only in the microamp range even at 100°C., the effect of reverse saturation current is usually negligible in most gate designs using silicon diodes. However, saturation currents remain a problem for designs using germanium diodes.

To understand clearly the consequences in a given circuit brought about by the variations in diode characteristics, power supply voltages, resistor values, logic levels, etc., it is usually necessary to resort to *worst-case analysis*. In worst-case analysis, we analyze the circuit using the particular combination of parameter values which will result in an extreme value of the desired variable.

As a very elementary example, let us consider the circuit and diode characteristics shown in Fig. 5.13. Assume that the resistor R

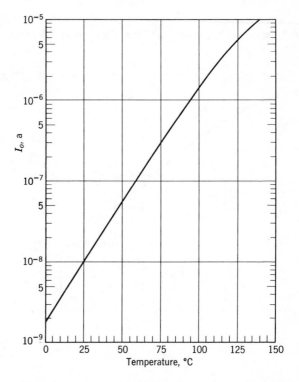

Fig. 5.12. Typical reverse saturation current, I_o, for a silicon diode.

can have a value between R(max) and R(min) because of manufacturing tolerance, and that the supply voltage E can lie between E(max) and E(min). If load lines representing R(max) and R(min) are drawn from the points E(min) and E(max) on the graph in Fig. 5.13*b*, the common area between the diode curves and load lines (shown as cross-hatched) will represent the loci of all possible operating points for the circuit in (*a*). The worst-case limits for V_{out} and I_F are indicated in the figure.

One additional consideration is of importance in diode logic. The capacitance of the diode and the storage time of the minority

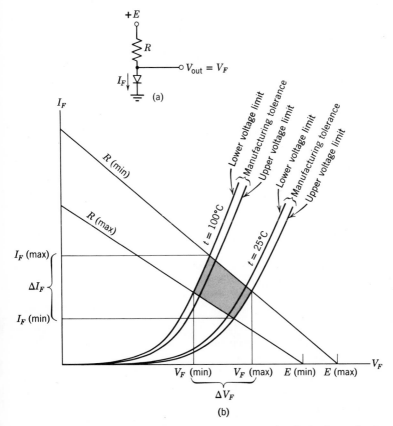

Fig. 5.13. Graphical analysis of the worst-case operating limits for a simple resistor-diode circuit.

carriers combine to limit the speed of the diode gate. These effects may be reduced by lowering the value of the load resistor to provide a lower resistance charging and recovery path.

5.3 DESIGN PROBLEMS IN DIODE LOGIC CIRCUITS

In this section some of the considerations involved in the design of diode logic circuits are discussed. Two fundamental problems become apparent in the course of the discussion. First, the lack cf isolation between diode gates tightly interlocks the design of the individual gates. Second, the lack of gain in the system imposes severe constraints on the design. For these reasons diode gates with more than four levels are uncommon. As we shall see in Chapters 6 and 7, gates made up of active elements have both gain and isolation, and thus have almost completely replaced multi-level diode gates in present-day digital systems.*

Throughout this section, the diode AND gate (positive representation) is used as a vehicle for discussion; the extension of the analysis to the OR gate is relatively straightforward, and hence is covered mainly in the problems at the end of the chapter. For simplicity we assume that all diodes in a given gate are identical, an assumption that is well justified for present-day silicon planar devices.

Table 5.1 and Fig. 5.14 define the variables in the problem. Each

TABLE 5.1

Variable	Symbol
Load current	I_L
Source voltage	
"Zero" level	V_{I0}
"One" level	V_{I1}
Source current	I_S
Power supply voltage	E_1
Diode forward voltage	V_F
Diode forward current	I_F
Diode reverse saturation current	
(defined positive)	I_o

* This section is designed both to provide further insight into the operation of diode gates and to serve as an introduction to the methods of worst-case analysis and design. However, on the basis that diode gates are not as common as transistor gates in present-day design, the text has been written so that the section can be omitted without serious loss of continuity.

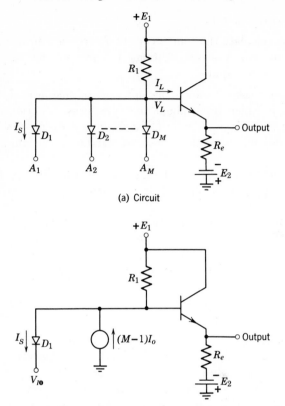

(a) Circuit

(b) Circuit state for worst-case source loading

Fig. 5.14. Diode logic AND gate driving an emitter follower.

of these variables can have a maximum and a minimum value depending on such factors as manufacturing tolerances, temperature, and the state of the load circuit and driving circuit. Clearly, some of these variables may assume either positive or negative values; in order to avoid confusion, the terms "maximum" and "minimum" are applied in an *algebraic* sense (that is, -6 is less than $+3$).

The exact value of the load current I_L is, of course, determined by the network being driven by this gate; for instance, another AND gate, an OR gate, or a transistor. To keep the present discussion relatively simple, we first assume that the AND gate is driving an emitter follower, as shown in Fig. 5.14a.

5.3.1 *Source Current*

Let us calculate the source current I_S required to operate this circuit, under worst-case conditions. To carry out such an analysis, three steps are required.

(1) We must determine the *states of the nonlinear elements* in the circuit which bring about the worst-case conditions for the variable in question. This usually involves deciding which input variables should be at the "zero" level and which should be at the "one" level.

(2) The circuit can now be analyzed in this state to find the relationship between the circuit parameters and the variable in question, in this case the source current I_S.

(3) The worst-case conditions of supply voltages, resistor values, etc. are now applied to the equation just derived. The appropriate worst-case condition for a given parameter can often be found by inspection from the equation, but at worst it can be obtained by partial differentiation. When appropriate, we must check to insure that the worst-case values are not sufficiently extreme to change the states of the nonlinear elements as determined in (1).

A little thought will show that the maximum value of I_S in the indicated direction, denoted by I_S (max), will occur when the gate output is in the "zero" state (positive representation) and diode A_1 is forward biased, while the other diodes are reverse biased. This, then, is the required worst-case state of the circuit. The input voltage values needed to produce this state are $A_1 = V_{I0}$ and $A_2 = A_3 = \cdots = A_M = V_{I1}$.

To find the relation between I_S and the circuit parameters for this circuit state, shown explicitly in Fig. 5.14b, we first represent the "load" on diode D_1 by a Thévenin equivalent. For simplicity here we assume that the emitter follower does not load the gate. Then the Thévenin resistance faced by D_1 is

$$R_{eq} = R_1 \tag{5.1}$$

and the Thévenin source voltage is, by inspection of Fig. 5.14b

$$E_{eq} = E_1 + (M - 1)I_o R_1 - V_{I0} \tag{5.2}$$

where M is defined as the *fan-in* of the gate, that is, the number of diode inputs that join together at the central node.

The current I_S can now be found graphically by drawing on a set of diode characteristics similar to Fig. 5.13*b* the load line corresponding to a resistor R_{eq} and a voltage E_{eq}. It is clear from Fig. 5.13*b* that the worst case of source loading, that is, the case yielding the most diode current for the given Thévenin load, occurs at maximum diode temperature, and at the lower voltage limit of the manufacturing tolerance range. Thus, these conditions define the appropriate curve to use in the graphical analysis.

Clearly I_S will be maximum if E_{eq} is maximum. Thus, the appropriate values to use in Eq. 5.2 are

$$E_1 = E_1(\text{max})$$
$$I_o = I_o(\text{max})$$
$$V_{I0} = V_{I0}(\text{min})$$

The term containing R_1 in Eq. 5.2 is usually not the dominant term, in which case R_1 should be at its minimum value, $R_1(\text{min})$.

5.3.2 *Output Current (Fan-out)*

Somewhat different considerations arise if we wish to calculate the output current capability of a diode AND gate, that is, the limitation on the amount of load current that can be drawn from the circuit. We assume that the circuit must be designed to drive arbitrary loads, so we must consider both positive and negative values of load current I_L. Appropriate circuit diagrams are shown in Fig. 5.15, in which the load is represented by a variable current source.

(*a*) *Positive load current.* Let us first find the limitations on positive load current, which might arise if the gate were driving an OR gate. For fixed input voltage levels $A_1, A_2, \ldots, A_M$, the fundamental circuit limitation on positive load current I_L is that, as the load current is increased, the output voltage level V_L in Fig. 5.15*a* drops until the diodes which are supposed to be on, become reverse biased. At this point the output voltage level becomes virtually independent of the input voltage level and the gate ceases to function properly. For this reason we must set a lower limit or threshold on the forward current in each ON diode to insure that the diodes do not change state. That is, the diodes which are supposed to be on must remain on and thus maintain the output voltage within the proper range. Call this threshold

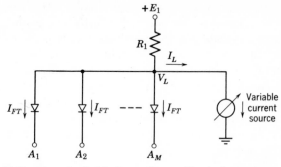

(a) Worst case circuit state for supplying positive load current

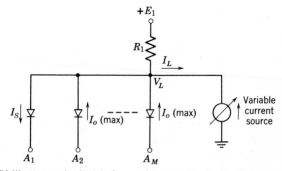

(b) Worst case circuit state for supplying negative load current

Fig. 5.15. Calculation of the limiting permissible load current of a diode AND gate.

diode current I_{FT}. The worst-case circuit state for supplying positive load current occurs for all diodes on, and drawing a current I_{FT}, as specified above.

Having set the diode states, we can now relate the load current I_L to the circuit parameters in this state. Summing the currents at the central node in Fig. 5.15a, we obtain

$$I_L = \frac{E_1 - (V_I + V_{FT})}{R_1} - M I_{FT} \qquad (5.3)$$

where V_{FT} is the diode forward drop corresponding to the prescribed diode threshold current I_{FT}. Clearly I_L can have a range of values depending on the circuit parameters. We are looking here for the *lower bound* of I_L when the diode forward currents are at their smallest permissible values. From Eq. 5.3 the worst case occurs when the output is in the "**1**" state:

$$V_I = V_{I1}(\text{max})$$
$$E_1 = E_1(\text{min})$$
$$R_1 = R_1(\text{max})$$

Also, the diode drop V_{FT} should be maximum for the given current I_{FT}. Thus we determine V_{FT} from the low-temperature diode characteristic, at the upper voltage limit of the diode tolerance range.

Clearly if the output is in the "zero" state, the circuit can supply a much larger load current (see Problem P5.4a).

(b) *Negative load current.* Let us now find the limitation on negative load current. The load current would be negative if, for example, the AND gate under consideration were used to drive another AND gate, as can be seen from the discussion in Sec. 5.3.1. Referring to Fig. 5.15b, most of the load current flowing *into* the summing node must flow through the diodes into the signal source, since we insist that the output voltage V_L stay within a specified range. Thus, the limitation on I_L in this case arises from a limitation on the maximum source current I_S, a problem we have already considered in Sec. 5.3.1.

A little thought will show that the worst-case condition for calculating the limiting value of permissible negative load current occurs when the output is in the "zero" state, the same condition specified for calculating $I_S(\text{max})$ in Sec. 5.3.1 (see Problem P. 5.4b). Thus, the worst-case state of the circuit is one diode input at V_{I0}, and all other diodes off; for example, $A_1 = V_{I0}$, and $A_2 = \ldots A_M = V_{I1}$. Summing the currents at the central node and solving for I_L, we obtain

$$I_L = -I_S(\text{max}) + \frac{E_1 - V_{I0} - V_{FS}}{R_1} + (M - 1)I_o \quad (5.4)$$

where V_{FS} is the forward diode drop corresponding to the specified diode current $I_S(\text{max})$. The worst-case conditions are clearly the same as those in Sec. 5.3.1.

The appropriate value of load current calculated above (Eqs. 5.3 or 5.4) can be used to determine the number of diode AND or

OR gates or transistor circuits that can be driven by this AND gate. This number, designated by N, is called the *fan-out* of a gate. It is clear from the above-cited equations that if the supply voltage E_1 is much larger than the signal source voltage levels V_{I0} and V_{I1} (which is the usual case), then the fan-out will be determined primarily by the supply voltage E_1 and the summing resistor R_1, and only secondarily by the spread (max-min) in the various voltage levels.

Equation 5.4 indicates that if an AND gate is used to drive other AND gates, then $|I_L| < |I_S(\text{max})|$; thus, the fan-out may be quite restricted. To achieve any fan-out greater than one, the current levels in the second gate must be substantially lower than those in the first gate.

5.3.3 *Selection of a Summing Resistor*

The two preceding subsections have been concerned with diode AND gate analysis to find the limits on source current and load current. In this section we consider an aspect of diode gate *design*: how to choose the value of the summing resistor R_1, given the maximum allowable source current $I_S(\text{max})$ and worst-case conditions of loading by other AND or OR gates. In this section we assume that the design must allow for either AND or OR gate loads. Somewhat less stringent circuit constraints result if it is known in advance that the AND gate will drive only other AND gates, or only other OR gates.

(a) *Calculation of $R_1(max)$*. Let us first calculate the maximum allowable value of R_1, designated as $R_1(\text{max})$. The upper limit on R_1 is set by the condition that the current through R_1 must be sufficient to supply the required positive load current and still maintain a minimum forward current I_{FT} in the diodes (i.e., the diodes must not change state). This is the same condition we imposed in Sec. 5.3.2.*a*. The worst-case of positive load current will clearly be imposed by an OR gate load, Fig. 5.16, with diode D_x on and diodes D_y and D_z off. The load V–I characteristics are thus given by the equation

$$I_L \cong (V_L + E_3)G_3$$

where for simplicity we neglect the diode drop in the OR gate. (Note that G_3 and E_3 can, if necessary, represent the Thévenin

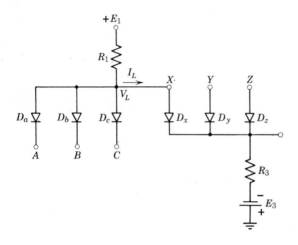

Fig. 5.16. Diode AND gate driving an OR gate.

equivalent of a more complicated load on the OR gate.) By summing currents at the V_L node, and solving for R_1, we obtain

$$R_1 = \frac{E_1 - V_I - V_{FT}}{(V_I + V_{FT} + E_3)G_3 + MI_{FT}} \tag{5.5}$$

where in Fig. 5.16 the fan-in M equals 3. Equation 5.5 will yield a number of values for R_1 depending on the parameter values assumed. We are interested here in the *lower bound* of this set of values, for this is the maximum value of R_1 which will still insure proper operation under worst-case conditions. We find by inspection of Eq. 5.5 that the lower bound is realized if

$$E_1 = E_1(\text{min})$$
$$V_I = V_{II}(\text{max})$$
$$E_3 = E_3(\text{max})$$
$$G_3 = G_3(\text{max})$$

Also, to maximize V_{FT} for the given diode current I_{FT} we assume D_a, D_b, and D_c are at a low temperature, at the upper voltage limit of the tolerance range. The value of R_1 cannot be any larger than that given by Eq. 5.5 with the above-listed parameter values, and still deliver the required minimum current to the diodes D_a, D_b, and D_c under worst-case conditions. If, on the other hand, the load resistor R_1 were smaller than $R_1(\text{max})$, then both the load current and the currents through diodes D_a, D_b, and D_c would increase, and the output voltage would rise somewhat.

(b) *Calculation of $R_1(min)$*. Clearly, there must also be a lower limit on the value of R_1 [designated $R_1(\text{min})$]. As mentioned above, when R_1 is reduced, the diode currents increase, and thus the lower limit on R_1 is set by the maximum diode current, or the maximum source current $I_S(\text{max})$. The conditions for worst-case source loading occur when one diode carries all the current, as, for example, $A = V_{I0}$, and $B = C = V_{I1}$ (see Sec. 5.3.1). The source loading is further aggravated if the AND gate is driving another AND gate, Fig. 5.17. The worst-case condition on the second AND gate is that only diode D_x is conducting. Thus, the appropriate load V–I relation is

$$I_L \cong (V_L - E_2)G_2$$

if we again neglect diode drops in the second gate.

Summing the currents at node V_L, we obtain

$$R_1 = \frac{E_1 - V_{I0} - V_{FS}}{I_S(\text{max}) + [V_{I0} + V_{FS} - E_2]G_2 - (M - 1)I_o} \quad (5.6)$$

where V_{FS} is the forward diode drop corresponding to the diode current $I_S(\text{max})$. This equation yields a range of values for R_1, depending on the exact values of E_1, etc. We are interested here in

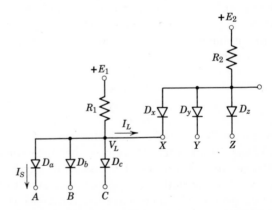

Fig. 5.17. Diode AND gate driving another AND gate.

the *upper bound* on this range to insure operation under worst-case conditions. From Eq. 5.6, these worst-case conditions are

$$E_1 = E_1(\text{max})$$
$$V_{I0} = V_{I0}(\text{min})$$
$$E_2 = E_2(\text{max})$$
$$I_o = I_o(\text{max})$$
$$G_2 = G_2(\text{max}) \quad \text{(because the term in brackets is negative)}$$

(c) *Numerical example.* The following numerical example of a five-diode AND circuit will serve to illustrate the calculations of $R_1(\text{max})$ and $R_1(\text{min})$. Assume that the variables have the ranges of values shown in Table 5.2.

TABLE 5.2

Variable	Symbol	Maximum Value	Minimum Value
Temperature	T	100°C.	25°C.
Source voltage			
"Zero" level	V_{I0}	−4.5 volts	−5.5 volts
"One" level	V_{I1}	+5.5 volts	+4.5 volts
Power supply voltage	E_1, E_2, E_3	+33 volts	+27 volts
Gate resistors	R_2, R_3	20 k	25 k

The supply voltages have been chosen to be greater than five times the basic logic level of five volts, in order to keep the currents through the summing resistors and hence the diode currents reasonably constant with changes in the output state. Clearly this practice tends to keep the output voltage levels more closely related to the input voltage levels by minimizing changes in diode forward voltage drops.

The values of $I_S(\text{max})$ and V_{FS}, and I_{FT} and V_{FT}, are chosen partly on the basis of the same considerations, i.e., minimizing the changes in diode forward voltage drop, and partly on the basis of source loading. Note from Fig. 5.10 that by keeping the diode current between 0.1 ma and 6 ma, the change in diode voltage drop is less than 200 mv. Assuming that 6 ma is not an excessive current to draw from the source, we set $I_S(\text{max}) = 6$ ma and $I_{FT} = 0.1$ ma. We defined V_{FS} as the forward voltage drop at high temperatures corresponding to a diode current of $I_S(\text{max})$; and thus from Figs. 5.10 and 5.11, $V_{FS} = 0.6$ volts. Recall also that V_{FT} is the forward diode drop at low temperatures corresponding to a diode current I_{FT}; and thus, from Fig. 5.10 $V_{FT} = 0.51$ volts. Finally, from Fig. 5.12, $I_o = 10$ na at 25°C. and 1.5 μa at 100°C. Substituting these values into Eqs. 5.5 and 5.6, we obtain

$$R_1(\text{max}) = \frac{27 - 5.5 - 0.51}{(5.5 + 0.51 + 33)0.04 + 5 \times 0.1} = 10.2 \text{ kilohms}$$

(units of volts, milliamps, kilohms, millimhos)

$$R_1(\text{min}) = \frac{33 + 5.5 - 0.6}{6 + (-5.5 + 0.6 - 33)0.04 - 4 \times 0.001} = 8.2 \text{ kilohms}$$

(units of volts, milliamps, kilohms, millimhos)

Note from Eqs. 5.5 and 5.6 that $R_1(\text{max})$ and $R_1(\text{min})$ are quite independent in that they contain different network parameters. If the calculated values are incompatible, i.e., $R_1(\text{max}) < R_1(\text{min})$, then some change must be made in the network parameters to achieve a workable solution. On the other hand, if $R_1(\text{max}) \gg R_1(\text{min})$, then the design is probably too conservative; for example, perhaps we have allowed too much loading on the source.

5.3.4 *Response Time of Diode Gates*

Our previous consideration of diode gates and their design took into account loading effects only for dc conditions. The dynamic loading which results from charging and discharging the load capacitance will impose an additional constraint on the choice of impedance level of the gate network. There are two charge-storage mechanisms which influence the response time of diode gates: charge-storage in the neutral regions and the space-charge regions of the diodes, and capacitive effects associated with the rest of the network. Charge-storage effects in modern high-speed diodes have been reduced to such an extent that the response time of most diode gates is now governed almost entirely by wiring capacitance and load capacitance effects. In Fig. 5.18 these various capacitances have been lumped into one effective load capacitor, C.

(a) *Rise-time calculations.* Let us first calculate the rise time of the AND gate in Fig. 5.18a. We shall analyze the condition in which initially the gate output is in the zero state, with diode D_1 on

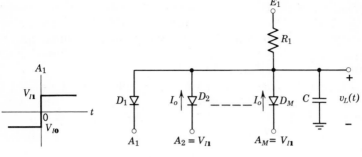

(a) AND gate with capacitive load

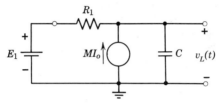

(b) Equivalent circuit for charge $(t > 0)$

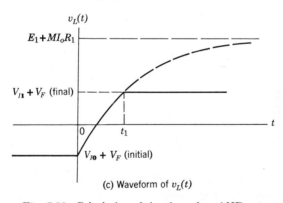

(c) Waveform of $v_L(t)$

Fig. 5.18. Calculation of rise time of an AND gate.

$(A_1 = V_{I0})$ and all other diodes off $(A_2 = A_3 \ldots = A_M = V_{I1})$. After the transient is over, i.e. when the gate output has reached the "one" state, all diodes will be on and conducting equally $(A_1 = A_2 = \ldots A_M = V_{I1})$.

At $t = 0$ the voltage A_1 suddenly changes from V_{I0} to V_{I1}. Because the voltage on the capacitor C cannot change instantaneously, the effect of the positive voltage step will be to turn off the diode D_1. The capacitor begins to charge through R_1 and the output voltage rises exponentially. The charging continues until the output voltage rises above V_{I1} at which time all of the diodes will turn on.

A circuit model appropriate during the charging interval is shown in Fig. 5.18b. The current source MI_o represents the reverse current of all of the diodes. The circuit as shown assumes no load on the gate, other than the capacitor, but, it is a simple matter to include the effects of loading, as we shall see later. By inspection, the voltage $v_L(t)$ will be a simple exponential, rising toward the voltage $E_1 + MI_oR_1$ with a time-constant R_1C, as shown in Fig. 5.18c. Note that the diode reverse current *speeds up* the transient. The initial condition

$$v_L|_{t=0^-} = V_{I0} + V_F(\text{initial}) \tag{5.7}$$

[where V_F(initial) is the diode voltage drop before the transient] completes the characterization of the output waveform:

$$v_L(t) = (E_1 + MI_oR_1)(1 - e^{-t/R_1C}) + [v_{I0} + V_F(\text{initial})]e^{-t/R_1C} \tag{5.8}$$

This equation applies until time t_1 in Fig. 5.18c, at which time (to a first approximation) the diodes all turn on and the output voltage becomes

$$v_L = V_{I1} + V_F(\text{final}) \tag{5.9}$$

where V_F(final) is the voltage drop across the diodes in the "one" state.

By equating Eqs. 5.8 and 5.9, we can find the time t_r, the rise time of the circuit. The result is

$$t_r = t_1 = R_1C \ln\left[\frac{E_1 + MI_oR_1 - V_{I0} - V_F(\text{initial})}{E_1 + MI_oR_1 - V_{I1} - V_F(\text{final})}\right] \tag{5.10a}$$

which for small I_o and small diode drop compared to E_1 can be simplified to

$$t_r \cong R_1C \ln\left[\frac{E_1 - V_{I0}}{E_1 - V_{I1}}\right] \tag{5.10b}$$

For $E_1 \gg V_{I0}$, V_{I1}, Eq. 5.10b further reduces to

$$t_r \cong \frac{R_1 C}{E_1} (V_{I1} - V_{I0}) \qquad (5.10c)$$

This result can be obtained by inspection from Fig. 5.19a by assuming that the capacitor is being charged by a current source E_1/R_1. The time t_r then corresponds to the time required for the capacitor voltage to change from V_{I0} to V_{I1}.

In the preceding derivation we assumed that there was no resistive loading on the gate. Fortunately, it is a relatively simple matter to include the effects of loading in the calculations. If the loading can be assumed to be linear, then E_1 and R_1 in Fig. 5.18b and Eqs. 5.8 and 5.10 should be replaced by the Thévenin equivalent of E_1, R_1, and the load. If the load is nonlinear, the problem can be solved as a succession of linear problems by employing piecewise linear analysis. Note that in either case, load current flowing *out* at the output terminals will *slow down* the transient whereas load current flowing *in* will *speed it up* (think of the current source MI_o in Fig. 5.18b as representing a load current).

In drawing the circuit in Fig. 5.18a, we assumed that the diode capacitance was negligible compared to wiring and load capacitance. If this is not true, some modification of the solution is required. In particular, capacitance associated with diode D_1 will couple the step at $t = 0$ directly through to the output. This will change the initial condition of the transient, but the waveform for v_L for t greater than zero remains a simple exponential (see Problem P5.6).

It is clear from Eq. 5.10b that the rise time can be reduced by lowering the value of the summing resistor R_1. Thus, on the basis of the derivation in Sec. 5.3.3b, particularly Eq. 5.6, there is a trade-off in the design of the AND gate between source loading and rise time.

b) *Fall-time calculations.* It can be seen from Fig. 5.18 that the fall time of the AND gate can be made quite short, because the capacitor C can be discharged rapidly through one or more forward-biased diodes. Thus, the fall time is governed directly by the current capability of the signal source and the forward resistance of the diode.

The rise and fall times of a diode OR gate are calculated in a fashion similar to that of the example for the AND gate. The principal difference is that the *rise* time is now governed by the signal source current rating, while the *fall* time is related to the RC time constant for the network (see Problems P5.7 and P5.8).

It should be noted that at the times of turn-on or turn-off of the diodes, the actual currents flowing may be rather complex functions of the network parameters. Often the nonlinear behavior of the diodes will cause rounding of the corners of the waveforms, and the inductance of the wiring will cause small overdamped oscillations. Because of this, the actual waveform for $v_L(t)$ will be somewhat more complicated than the results derived in this section.

PROBLEMS

P5.1 Resistor logic is often used to construct a *majority gate*, the output of which is +1 volt only when a majority of the inputs are at +1 volt. Modify the circuit in Fig. 5.3 so that it will perform this operation.

P5.2 Draw the diagram of the resistor logic circuit to realize the circle sum function $F = A \oplus B$ using:
  (a) A direct inverter.
  (b) An inverted Schmitt-trigger detector.

P5.3 Write the Boolean equation and draw the diagram of a resistor logic circuit to detect the situation when exactly 3 out of 5 input signals are in the 1-state. Under this condition, a 1-state output should result. Inverters may be used.

P5.4 (a) What is the maximum permissible positive load current that can be drawn from the output of an AND circuit for the output in the "zero" state, while still maintaining proper gate voltage levels under worst-case conditions? See Fig. 5.15a. Compare with Sec. 5.3.2.a.
  (b) Calculate the largest permissible load current that can flow *into* an AND gate when the output is in the "one" state without the source current exceeding a value $I_S(\max)$. See Figure 5.15b. Compare with Eq. 5.4.

P5.5 (a) Derive the equation for the maximum and minimum summing resistance of a diode logic OR gate under conditions similar to those for the AND gate in Sec. 5.3.3.
  (b) Derive the equation for maximum signal source loading of an OR gate.

P5.6 Calculate the rise time of the diode AND gate in Sec. 5.3.4, assuming that diode charge-storage effects can be represented by a small fixed capacitor across each diode.

P5.7 Calculate the rise and fall times for a diode OR gate.

P5.8 Calculate the rise and fall times for a simple two-input diode AND gate driving one of the inputs of a two-input diode OR gate.

6

Active Logic Circuits

6.0 INTRODUCTION

The five common types of active logic circuits that will be considered in this chapter are

Resistor-Transistor Logic	RTL
Diode-Transistor Logic	DTL
Direct-Coupled-Transistor Logic	DCTL
Transistor-Transistor Logic	TTL
Current-Mode Logic	CML

For reasons of low power consumption and simplicity, *RTL*, *DTL*, *DCTL*, and *TTL* circuits usually operate with the transistors in the saturated mode, and thus the following descriptions will be treated primarily from this point of view. It is entirely possible, however, to design similar circuits which use diode clamps or carefully controlled operating points so as to avoid saturation. For example, *CML* circuits, which will be described in Sec. 6.4, are operated in this manner.

Logic circuits can be designed to operate in any one of the three basic amplifier configurations, i.e., common-base, common-collector, or common-emitter. For reasons of power gain, the common-emitter connection is principally used in logic circuits. With one exception, (TTL), all the logic circuits to be described use the common-emitter connection.

Many of the problems which arise in the described circuits may be overcome through the use of more sophisticated circuitry. With the increased use of integrated circuits, the greater number of transistors which are required in these more complex circuits is no longer a handicap. In integrated circuits it is frequently as simple to fabricate a transistor as a resistor, whereas it may be extremely difficult to provide either inductors or large-value capacitors.

6.1 RESISTOR-TRANSISTOR LOGIC (RTL)

The linear addition of binary signals in a resistive network has been described in Sec. 5.1. It was noted that severe limitations of this technique resulted from the requirements placed on the detector and level restorer. By connecting a transistor to the output of an appropriately designed resistive network, we can simultaneously improve sensitivity, achieve current and voltage gain, and provide level restoration. This kind of circuit is called Resistor-Transistor Logic (*RTL*).

6.1.1 *Basic RTL Gate*

Figure 6.1 shows the basic circuit arrangement for an *RTL* gate. Clearly, if a positive signal is applied to any of the inputs, collector current will flow causing the output voltage (V_{out}) to fall to the voltage

$$V_{\text{out}} = V_{CC} - I_C R_L \qquad \text{(not saturated)} \qquad (6.1)$$

If the base drive is sufficient, the collector junction will saturate and the output voltage becomes

$$V_{\text{out}} = V_{CE}(\text{sat}) \qquad \text{(saturated)} \qquad (6.2)$$

Once the transistor is in the saturation region, the output voltage becomes relatively constant and independent of the base current drive. Under this condition, if positive signals are now also applied to the other inputs, the result is to drive the transistor deeper into saturation. The output voltage will, however, change

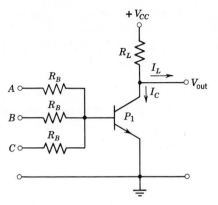

Fig. 6.1. Basic *RTL* NOR gate. Boolean output is $F = (A + B + C)' = A'B'C'$.

only slightly. This saturated state may be defined as the Boolean "0" (positive representation will be used throughout this chapter unless otherwise noted) and will be a relatively narrow band of voltage values around a nominal $V_{CE}(\text{sat})$.

Let us now assume that signals, representing a Boolean "0" as described above, are applied to all the inputs of the gate in Fig. 6.1. The emitter-base junction will be forward biased by a voltage equal to $V_{CE}(\text{sat})$, which may be 50 to 100 mv for germanium transistors and 100 to 300 mv for silicon transistors. Such low forward-bias voltages result in an extremely small value for the collector current I_C. As a result, the output voltage will rise toward V_{CC} and, assuming no output load current, will become

$$V_{\text{out}} = V_{CC} - I_C R_L \cong V_{CC} \tag{6.3}$$

To be a useful logic circuit the gate must drive some load. An additional current (I_L) will flow through R_L, causing the output voltage to drop below the value of V_{out} given by Eq. 6.3. The output now becomes

$$V_{\text{out}} = V_{CC} - (I_C + I_L)R_L \tag{6.4}$$

This output voltage is defined as the Boolean "1" and clearly may fall within a band of values ranging downward from V_{CC}. To insure that the output voltage values representing a "0" and "1" are unambiguous, it is necessary to generate design rules for the permissible loading. Clearly, the minimum value for the "**1**" state should be greater than the maximum value of $V_{CE}(\text{sat})$ which represents the "**0**" state. This provides for the required "forbidden" region described in Sec. 1.0.

6.1.2 *Modified RTL Gate*

As noted in Sec. 2.1.3, the use of clamp diodes can improve the speed of response of a transistor circuit, and stabilize the collector voltage when the transistor is off. An example of this is shown in Fig. 6.2, where a diode clamp has been added to the collector of an *RTL* gate. The voltage V_{CL} is normally considerably lower than V_{CC}. Thus when the circuit is in the "**1**" state, the output voltage will be approximately equal to V_{CL}, relatively independent of the load connected to the gate if the load current is small enough so that the clamp diode is forward biased by the current through R_L.

A bias resistor, which is connected to a separate bias supply, insures that the transistor is turned completely off, even with $V_{CE}(\text{sat})$ applied to the inputs, A, B, and C. In addition, the turn-off time is decreased because the negative base current provides reverse overdrive.

6.1.3 *Fan-out for RTL Cascade*

A somewhat different constraint appears when the *RTL* gate is used *only* to drive other *RTL* gates, as shown in Fig. 6.3a. When

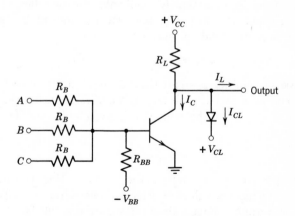

Fig. 6.2. Modified *RTL* NOR gate.

P is cut off, it is necessary that V_{out} be positive enough to drive the Q transistors into saturation. Provided that this condition is met, the precise value of V_{out} is no longer of direct interest, because now the representation is in terms of either the *states* of transistors $Q_1, \ldots, Q_N$ or the voltages $V_{Q1}, \ldots, V_{QN}$, and not in terms of V_{out}.

To insure saturation of transistors $Q_1, \ldots, Q_N$ (assumed identical),

$$I_B(Q) \geqslant \frac{V_{CC}}{\beta_F R_{LQ}} \tag{6.5}$$

hence

$$V_{BE}(Q) \geqslant V_{BEO} \tag{6.6}$$

where V_{BEO} is by definition the *base-to-emitter voltage at the edge of saturation*. When P has a voltage $V_{CE}(\text{sat})$ applied at all its inputs,

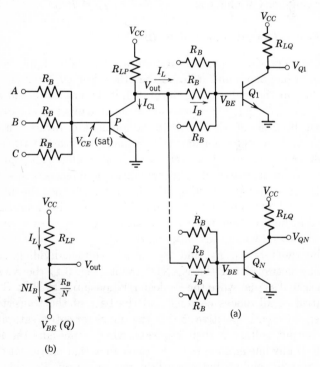

Fig. 6.3. (*a*) RTL gate in "1" state driving N other gate transistors. (*b*) Model for the *RTL* gate in the "1" state driving a fan-out of N other gate transistors.

then $V_{BE}(P) \cong V_{CE}(\text{sat})$, as shown in the figure, and the collector current of P will be so small that it can be neglected compared to I_L. Under these conditions the interstage coupling network can be redrawn as shown in Fig. 6.3b. Using this figure we find

$$\frac{V_{CC} - V_{BE}(Q)}{R_{LP} + R_B/N} = NI_B(Q) \tag{6.7}$$

By using the *equalities* in Eqs. 6.5 and 6.6 to eliminate $I_B(Q)$ and $V_{BE}(Q)$, we can solve Eq. 6.7 for N_{max}, the maximum number of RTL circuits that can be driven by gate P.

$$N_{\text{max}} = \beta_F \left(1 - \frac{V_{BEO}}{V_{CC}} \right) - \frac{R_B}{R_L} \tag{6.8}$$

(For simplicity we have assumed $R_L = R_{LP} = R_{LQ}$.)

6.2 DIODE-TRANSISTOR LOGIC (DTL)

Diode-Transistor Logic is a natural extension of diode logic (DL) on one hand, and RTL on the other. For DL circuits, there is a loss in the logic voltage-level definiteness as more and more gates are cascaded. There is also additional loading on the driving source because of the need to accommodate reverse leakage currents. It would seem natural, therefore, to place a transistor amplifier at the output of each gate, thus simultaneously providing isolation, increased driving capabilities, and reconstituted logic levels. Generally an inverting amplifier is used; hence the outputs become NAND and NOR functions. These gate circuits are illustrated in Figs. 6.4 and 6.5, where positive logic representation and positive signal voltage levels are used.

The resistors R_1, R_2, and R_3 form a voltage-dividing, level-shifting network. For the NAND circuit (Fig. 6.4) the resistors are selected so that when the Boolean relationship $\mathbf{A = B = C = 1}$ is satisfied, all diodes conduct and the base of the transistor is driven sufficiently positive so that the transistor enters saturation. The output voltage is then $V_{CE}(\text{sat})$, which represents the Boolean $\mathbf{0}$. If any one input goes to the Boolean $\mathbf{0}$, that particular diode continues to conduct but the others will be cut off. For this condition, it is required that the base have a negative voltage applied to it, thus turning the transistor off. The collector voltage rises

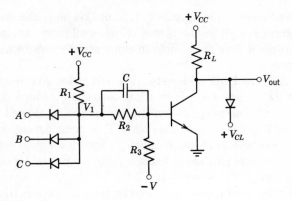

Fig. 6.4. *DTL* NAND gate. Boolean output for positive representation is $F = (ABC)' = A' + B' + C'$.

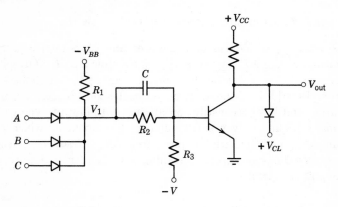

Fig. 6.5. *DTL* NOR gate. For positive representation, the Boolean output is $F = (A + B + C)'$.

toward V_{CC} until the clamp diode conducts, clamping the output to the logic level V_{CL}, which represents a Boolean 1. The capacitor C is a "speed up" capacitor which supplies overdrive current to the base thus improving the turn-on switching time. Excessive overdrive may, however, result in excessive storage delay and correspondingly slower turn-off time when the transistor is on for only a short time. These matters are discussed in Secs. 1.3 and 2.1.2.

The operation of the NOR gate in Fig. 6.5 is similar except that the level shifting network R_1, R_2, and R_3 is designed so that when any one or more of the inputs at A, B, or C is high, the transistor will be turned on; it will be turned off when all inputs are low. For some designs it may be possible to eliminate the resistor R_3 in the NOR gate.

If an AND and OR diode network are cascaded and then passed through the inverting amplifier, the arrangement is called "double-level gating." The composite circuit can then be considered to be a basic building block (see Fig. 6.6). This arrangement has the advantage of a smaller degeneration in logic level than would be the case for either gate alone, because there is a partial cancellation of diode voltage drops (see Sec. 5.2.4).

The fan-in of DTL gates is limited by the same factors that limit the fan-in of a diode gate (see Sec. 5.3). The fan-out in DTL gates is of course limited by the transistor circuit rather than the diodes.

6.3 DIRECT-COUPLED-TRANSISTOR LOGIC (DCTL)

Direct-Coupled-Transistor Logic uses transistors for the gating elements. Figure 6.7 shows the form of a simple $DCTL$ NOR gate. It is seen that in this gate the *transistors* act as the summing elements. In addition, the transistors in the $DCTL$ gate provide isolation and level reconstitution at each gate output. The gates normally require only a small number of components which are arranged in a particularly simple manner. As a result of its simplicity, $DCTL$ has special advantages for either miniature or "integrated" circuits.

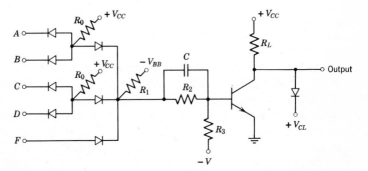

Fig. 6.6. DTL double-level gating. For positive representation, the Boolean output is **F = (AB + CD + F)′**.

DCTL circuits could be designed with the transistors operating in either the saturated or unsaturated mode. However, saturated circuitry has the advantages of a built-in availability of a "clamp level," high current carrying capacity, and low standby power. Saturated circuitry does, however, carry a price in terms of speed limitations imposed by the minority-carrier storage. For reasons of economy, simplicity, and low power, the nearly universal practice is to use *DCTL* gates in the saturated mode.

6.3.1 *NOR Gate*

Figure 6.8 shows the circuit for a *DCTL* NOR gate driving a fan-out of N other NOR gates. A positive voltage on any input, A, B, or C, will turn on P_1, P_2, or P_3 so that the output voltage of the P gate will fall to $V_{CE}(\text{sat})$. When all the inputs, A, B, and C are low, the voltage V_{CE1} rises toward V_{CC} until the driven transistors $Q_1, \ldots W_1$ turn on.

The correct operation of *DCTL* circuits is largely dependent on the following conditions.

(1) Resistors R_L and R_B must be of appropriate value to ensure that when the P gate is off, gates Q through W will be on.

(2) When the P gate is on, gates Q through W must be off. This requires

$$V_{BET} > V_{CE}(\text{sat}) \tag{6.9}$$

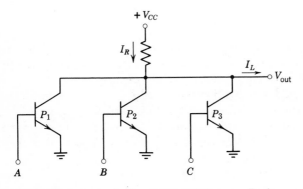

Fig. 6.7. Simplified form of the *DCTL* NOR gate. Boolean output is $\mathbf{F = (A + B + C)'}$.

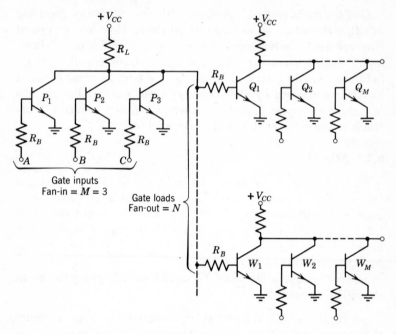

Fig. 6.8. *DCTL* three-input NOR gate driving N other gate transistors.

where V_{BET} is by definition the *base-to-emitter threshold voltage*, that is, the voltage at which the transistor just begins to conduct (see Sec. 7.3.3 for a more precise definition).

The difference between the two voltages V_{BET} and $V_{CE}(\text{sat})$ is the voltage margin, Δ_T. As we shall see, this voltage margin is directly related to the noise immunity of *DCTL* circuits, inasmuch as the addition of noise in excess of Δ may cause the circuit to enter the improper state (see Sec. 7.3 for details).

It should be noted that the states to which we refer are generated by the *transistor*, which must be "off" or "on" (saturated), respectively. These are fairly *definite* states which may be described more or less exactly by the transistor currents. In particular, the collector current in the "off" and "on" state may differ by many orders of magnitude; but this large current difference (and definite description of the operating region of the transistor) corresponds to a relatively *small* swing in collector voltage.

The base padding resistors R_B are included to equalize the base currents and thus reduce variations in performance due to unequal V_{BE} characteristics. This matter will be discussed in the next chapter, Secs. 7.2.4 and 7.2.5.

DCTL circuits are vulnerable to excessive collector leakage currents in the following way. The collector current which results from I_{CBO} will cause the output voltage to be lowered because of the drop across R_L. If this drop becomes excessive, the output may then be so low that it fails to turn on the transistors in the driven stage. This phenomenon is particularly important at high temperatures, and for germanium transistors. For very low power circuits this effect may become a limiting factor.

6.3.2 *NAND Gate*

Figure 6.9 is one form of a *DCTL* NAND gate. Current will flow through the cascaded transistors only if the voltages at the inputs A, B, and C are simultaneously "high." If there are M

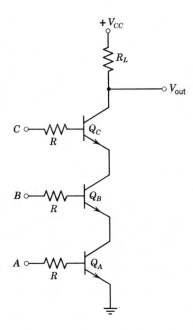

Fig. 6.9. *DCTL* NAND gate. Boolean output is $F = (ABC)'$.

identical transistors in the cascade, the input voltage required to turn on the uppermost transistor will be approximately

$$V = V_{BE} + [M - 1]V_{CE}(\text{sat}) \qquad (6.10)$$

Perhaps the most serious drawback to this circuit is the basic limitation on fan-in. When the gate is on, the output voltage will be $MV_{CE}(\text{sat})$. In order to insure that this voltage will not turn on a transistor driven by this gate, it is required that

$$MV_{CE}(\text{sat}) < V_{BET} \qquad (6.11)$$

It is possible to partially circumvent this difficulty by putting one or more diodes in series with each base driven by this gate, thus increasing the threshold voltage of the driven gate. However, this will require a higher drive voltage. Another approach is to increase the base drive current to the Q transistors, thus increasing saturation and lowering $V_{CE}(\text{sat})$. Both of these methods, however, result in greater power dissipation. For these reasons this form of *DCTL* NAND gate has not been used widely.

6.3.3 *DCTL Inverters and Buffers*

Because one element of a NOR gate is in fact an inverter, a multi-input gate is often used as an inverter by simply grounding the unused inputs or leaving them unconnected. A noninverting buffer is formed by connecting two such inverters in cascade.

6.3.4 *DCTL Flip-Flop (Bistable Multivibrator)*

Figure 6.10 shows a *DCTL* flip-flop with triggering transistors. This circuit can be formed by interconnecting two *DCTL* NOR gates. The connections are such that $V_{CE}(\text{sat})$ of the transistor on one side keeps the opposite transistor turned off. This results in base current for the ON transistor being supplied through the opposite load resistor.

6.3.5 *Limitations of DCTL Circuits*

The principal requirements for transistors in *DCTL* circuits are:

(1) Uniform transistor parameters, especially V_{BE}.
(2) Low I_{CBO}.
(3) Low $V_{CE}(\text{sat})$.
(4) Reasonable value of β_F (i.e., $\beta_F > 10$).

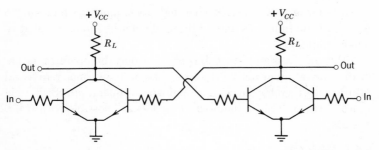

Fig. 6.10. *DCTL* flip-flop (bistable multivibrator) made by interconnecting NOR gates. The triggers are connected to the other gate inputs.

One principal disadvantage is the limited fan-in and fan-out (see Chap. 7). Another disadvantage is the poor noise immunity, resulting from the fact that V_{BET} is only slightly larger than $V_{CE}(\text{sat})$. At high temperatures this margin can be as low as 0.1 volt for silicon transistors. Because the supply and signal voltages are so small, the signal currents in the common ground or other adjacent conductors can result in "logic noise" voltages being developed across these conductors. These conductors may be common to many different circuits, so that coupling of logic noise into different parts of the logic system can occur, thus causing faulty operation. All of these matters are discussed in more detail in Chap. 7.

The *DCTL* logic circuitry was originally developed for use with germanium surface-barrier transistors. At that time severe limitations existed with regard to uniformity of V_{BE} characteristics, large magnitude of collector leakage and low beta. This required careful selection of transistors in order to achieve adequate noise margin. With the advent of planar, epitaxial silicon transistors, which have low collector leakage and high V_{BE} threshold voltage, *DCTL* circuitry is being used widely again. The reader is referred to Chapters 1 and 2 for the differences in limitations for silicon and germanium transistors.

6.4 CURRENT-MODE LOGIC (CML)

As discussed in Sec. 2.2.2, current-mode logic makes use of a constant current which is switched from one transistor to another.

Circuits using this "current steering" technique can be made to perform logic functions and additionally can be interconnected to make a flip-flop.

Although transistors in *CML* circuits may be operated either in the saturation or active region, it has been customary to avoid saturation, thereby achieving high-speed operation. Switching times of the order of 1 nanosecond or less are possible with *CML* circuits.

6.4.1 *Basic CML Gate*

Figure 6.11 shows the basic structure of a current-mode logic gate. Taken together, the resistor R_C and the voltage $-V_{CC}$ constitute an approximate current source I_O, which is injected at the node K. The circuit arrangement is similar to a difference amplifier.

Initially assume that a *negative* signal is applied to the inputs A, B, and C. Transistor Q_0, whose base is referenced to ground, will thus be on and have a collector current $I_C = I_O$ while the transistors Q_1, Q_2, and Q_3 will be turned off. If now one or more of the inputs A, B, or C is *positive*, the corresponding transistor(s) is turned on. Depending on the base-emitter threshold voltage (V_{BET}) and the beta of the transistors, only a small difference in logic voltage is required to cause the constant current I_O to switch from one side to the other in the circuit.

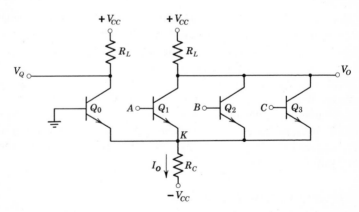

Fig. 6.11. *CML* gate. Note that both the OR and NOR logic functions are formed. That is, the Boolean outputs are $\mathbf{V_O = (A + B + C)'}$ and $\mathbf{V_Q =}$ $\mathbf{A + B + C}$.

It is clear that if saturation is to be avoided, there is a shift in the *level* of voltage representation of the logic from input to output. The *input* signal voltage must swing between some negative and some positive value, while the corresponding output voltage V_o is always positive. Neglecting the effect of any external load current, the output voltage levels are approximately

$$V_{01} = V_{CC} \tag{6.12}$$

$$V_{00} = V_{CC}\left(1 - \frac{R_L}{R_C}\right) \tag{6.13}$$

assuming $R_L \ll R_C$.

In order to allow the output of this gate to be coupled to the inputs of other such gates, it is necessary to shift the output voltage swing (by using a zener diode or a resistive voltage divider referenced to $-V_{CC}$) so that V_{00} and V_{01} will have negative and positive values respectively (see Sec. 2.2.3 and P6.2). Another technique is to use complementary gates. This complementary arrangement permits a *pnp* gate to drive a complementary *npn* gate directly, i.e., the signals levels are compatible. More discussion of this point will be found in Sec. 2.2.3.

6.4.2 *CML Circuit Variations*

A number of variations of the basic circuit shown in Fig. 6.11 are used. For example, the outputs may be clamped to fixed voltages to achieve precise output signal levels at a low impedance. It is common to replace the resistor R_C with an active current source, i.e., a common-base transistor. If the unprimed output is not needed, a diode can be used to replace Q_0 (see Sec. 2.2.2).

If the output of the gate in Fig. 6.11 is clamped to voltages which permit only a *very small* swing in the output signal, very high speed operation may be obtained. On the other hand if the clamping voltages are widely separated in value, the voltage representations for the logic signal will have a large "voltage margin" between them and hence will be quite immune to imposed noise. However, the larger signal swing will result in a reduced speed because of the larger charge storage *change* which occurs in circuit capacitances.

Advantage is sometimes taken of the differential nature of the *CML* circuit, to convey the signals between circuits with twisted pairs of wires. The input to Q_0 in Fig. 6.11 is connected to the "reference" side of the signal wire pair, thus achieving common-mode rejection and high noise immunity.

6.4.3 *CML Flip-Flop*

Figure 6.12 shows two basic *CML* inverter circuits interconnected as a *CML* flip-flop. Here the bias reference voltage is obtained from the opposite transistor. The coupling resistors are used to set the required on and off bias conditions (see Problem P6.3). Trigger transistors are also shown for inputs. Alternatively, triggering could be done at the bases by using a slightly different circuit.

6.4.4 *Advantages and Limitations of CML Circuits*

Because *CML* circuits are designed to operate in the active region, they tend to be faster than saturated circuits. When operated with large signal swings they will have high noise immunity (at some sacrifices in speed).

CML circuits are less dependent on the dc characteristics of transistors than are the logic circuits previously discussed. The

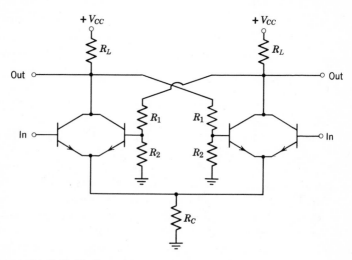

Fig. 6.12. *CML* flip-flop with input trigger transistors.

principal drawback to CML circuits is their relatively large power requirement and the larger number of components which are frequently required for a given logic function. CML circuits are usually used where the ultimate in speed and/or noise immunity is required.

6.5 TRANSISTOR-TRANSISTOR LOGIC (TTL)

All the previously described logic circuits have made use of common-emitter connected transistors. TTL circuits make use of the common-base connection. Figure 6.13 shows a simplified form of a TTL NAND gate. Transistors Q_1, Q_2, Q_3, and Q_4 operate as a gate that can either turn off or drive into saturation the output transistor Q_0. The emitters of the input transistors Q_1, Q_2, Q_3, and Q_4 are the gate inputs. The logic levels are approximately

$$V_0 = V_{CE}(\text{sat}) \tag{6.14}$$

$$V_1 = V_{CC} - I_L R_L \tag{6.15}$$

The value of V_{BB} is chosen so that for all specified loading conditions the following inequality is satisfied.

$$V_0 + V_{BEO} < V_{BB} < V_1 + V_{BET} \tag{6.16}$$

The left-hand side of Eq. 6.16 refers to the turn-on condition of $Q_1 \cdots Q_4$, while the right hand side refers to their turn-off condition. An additional requirement is that when Q_0 is on, the volt-

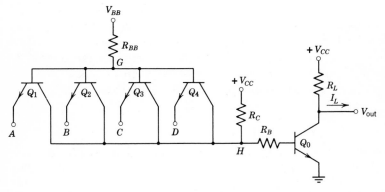

Fig. 6.13. Basic TTL NAND gate. The Boolean output is $\mathbf{F} = \mathbf{(ABCD)'}$.

age at the collector node H does not drop so low as to permit the collector-base junction, of say Q_1, to become forward biased.

Assuming positive representation, the output of the *TTL* gate in Fig. 6.13 is a NAND function of the input variables. The voltage swings at the base and collector nodes G and H both represent AND functions of the input variables, but for these nodes the voltage representation has shifted values, relative to the output voltage swing.

6.6 INTEGRATED LOGIC CIRCUITS

Many of the limitations in the logic circuits which have been described arise from the fact that in using discrete components it is usually desirable to minimize the total number of components for reasons of economy and reliability. Also, the usual wide manufacturing tolerance on transistors and diodes makes strict selection necessary in order to achieve high performance.

In integrated circuits some of these restrictions no longer apply so strongly. The cost of manufacturing an integrated circuit containing a dozen or more transistors may be competitive with the cost of a single transistor. It has also been demonstrated that such an integrated circuit may be no less reliable than a transistor.

For integrated circuits, it is frequently easier to fabricate a transistor than to fabricate a resistor of close tolerance or high value. Because of these factors, new and sophisticated logic circuits are being designed which make use of many more transistors than conventional circuits. In these circuits, transistors are often used to replace resistors, frequently as constant-current sources or as the collector load. In addition, in the design, advantage is taken of the greater uniformity of threshold voltages for transistors which are fabricated on a single integrated circuit chip.

An integrated circuit version of the *TTL* gate of Sec. 6.5 will be described in the following section.

6.6.1 *Integrated TTL Gate*

Shown in Fig. 6.14 is an integrated version of a *TTL* gate that nearly duplicates the input circuitry of the gate in Fig. 6.13. The multi-emitter input transistor is equivalent to Q_1, Q_2, Q_3, Q_4 in Fig. 6.13. The principal difference between this particular inte-

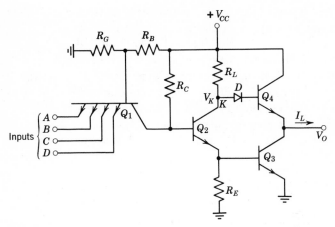

Fig. 6.14. Integrated *TTL* NAND gate which overcomes some of the limitations of the simpler discrete-element gates.

grated version and the *TTL* gate described in the previous section appears in the output circuit (which, of course, could have been duplicated for the discrete component example). The output logic voltage levels are approximately

$$V_{O0} = V_{CE}(\text{sat}) \tag{6.18}$$

$$V_{O1} = V_{CC} - V_{BE}(Q_4) - V_D - \frac{I_L}{\beta_F} R_L \tag{6.19}$$

The operation of the gate is as follows. When one or more of the inputs is "low", Q_1 will become saturated. This results in Q_2 and Q_3 being turned off. However, current flows through R_L and the diode D into the base of Q_4, turning it on. Transistor Q_4 is connected in the common-collector configuration, hence is capable of delivering a large positive current I_L.

If now all the input voltages are "high," transistor Q_1 will be turned off, assuming that R_B and R_G have been appropriately chosen, thereby saturating Q_2 and Q_3. The voltage at the node K thus becomes

$$V_K = V_{BE}(Q_3) + V_{CE}(\text{sat})(Q_2) \tag{6.20}$$

and the output becomes

$$V_O = V_{CE}(\text{sat}) \tag{6.21}$$

The purpose of the diode D may now be understood. If the diode were not present, Q_4 in this state would be forward-biased by a voltage $V_K - V_O = V_{BE}(Q_3)$ and thus would draw substantial current. Inclusion of the diode introduces in effect a diode voltage divider, thus reducing the input voltage of Q_4 to $V_{BE}(Q_3)/2$, with a corresponding large reduction in the collector current of Q_4. Two diodes in series would raise the threshold voltage even further and thus give increased operating margin.

Since Q_3 is now saturated, the circuit can support substantial *negative* load current. Because large load current capability exists for both the "high" and "low" states, the fan-out capacity is very large. An additional bonus arises from the fact that large currents, in either direction, are available to drive external capacitance. Hence *both* the rise and fall times can be quite small.

PROBLEMS

P6.1 Refer to Sec. 6.1.2. Find the expression for the maximum fan-out for the modified RTL gate in Fig. 6.2.

P6.2 (*a*) Design a resistive level shifting network for the output of the CML gate of Fig. 6.11, such that the voltage levels are symmetrical about 0 volts.

(*b*) Find the expression for the logic voltage swing which results from using this network.

(*c*) Find the Thévenin equivalent source impedance at the output of the level shifting network for the two logic levels.

P6.3 Find the values of R_1 and R_2 in the CML flip-flop of Fig. 6.12 such that proper bias conditions will exist. Assume the dc level of the input is approximately $V_{CC}/2$.

7

Design Problems in DCTL Circuits

7.0 INTRODUCTION

The previous chapter provided a qualitative description of some typical digital circuits. This chapter will attempt to give some insight into the kind of experimental and analytical techniques which are used in the design of digital circuits. We shall concentrate our attention on DCTL circuits because of the particularly simple circuit arrangement which permits a fairly direct circuit analysis. However, these problems are identical to, or at least typical of, many of the problems which arise in other forms of logic circuitry described in the last chapter. Only a few of the more important design problems will be considered; some of the considerations involved in dynamic switching between states have already been discussed in Chapters 1 and 2.

There are many different techniques which have been employed in the design of logic circuits. The Ebers-Moll large-signal model provides a fairly accurate picture of the dc conditions. Unfortunately, the nonlinear equations which result from a completely analytical approach can become quite complicated if the interaction and loading effects are considered. The most precise analysis technique in use today is a piecewise linear analysis. By carrying out the analysis on a computer, a sufficiently large number of "pieces" may be taken so as to approximate closely the nonlinear model. In such an accurate analysis, it is necessary to have a great deal of measured data for the characteristics of the actual components to be used. The analysis will usually include a fairly large section of the logic circuitry so that even weak interactions are taken into account.

We shall see that by using some very simple models, it is possible to derive reasonable guide lines for practical design. It should be remembered that no *one* analysis of this sort will predict the complete performance of the logic circuitry. However, by studying a number of these simple solutions, a reasonably complete picture can be assembled.

We shall not undertake a full worst-case analysis in this chapter. However, we will carry out the first two of the three steps required for such an analysis. Recall from Chapter 5 that these three steps are:

(1) Determine the states of the nonlinear elements in the circuit in order to bring about the worst-case conditions for the variable in question. This often involves deciding which of the input variables should be at the "zero" level and which should be at the "one" level. Sometimes it will not be obvious by inspection which states define the worst-case conditions. In these instances it will be necessary to analyze several possible circuit states to ascertain the worst case (see, for example, Sec. 7.5).

(2) Analyze this state to find the relationship between the circuit parameters and the variable in question.

(3) Apply the worst-case conditions of supply voltages, resistor values, etc., to the equation just derived. Often the appropriate worst-case condition for a given parameter can be found by inspection from the equation, but in any case it can be obtained by partial differentiation. To complete the process, we must check to insure that the worst-case values are not sufficiently extreme to change the states of the nonlinear elements as determined in (1).

As stated above, we shall undertake in this chapter only the first two of these steps. Because the third step—that of choosing the appropriate worst-case values of supply voltages, etc.—is quite straightforward, though sometimes tedious, it has not been included in the text discussion (see, however, Problem P7.3).

This chapter is organized into three principal sections, dealing with output parameters (fan-out), voltage margin, and input parameters (fan-in). Although these three parameters are not entirely independent, as we shall see, it is nevertheless convenient to treat them in separate sections so that the salient features of each may be linked together.

7.1 DC CONDITIONS FOR DCTL CIRCUITS

There are three principal dc conditions which must be met in order to insure proper operation of *DCTL* circuits:

(1) The available output current from a given gate must be equal to or greater than the maximum current required to drive subsequent circuits.

(2) The spread in V_{BE} vs. I_B characteristics must be sufficiently small to insure reasonably uniform base drives to transistors with paralleled inputs.

(3) There must be an adequate voltage margin between the $V_{CE}(\text{sat})$ of an ON transistor and the V_{BET} (base-emitter threshold voltage) of an OFF transistor, so that two unambiguous states may be realized.

The first condition is related to power and speed trade-offs, the second to the uniformity of transistor characteristics, and the third to noise immunity. Since there is an interrelation between these parameters, it is necessary to carry out an iterative design process so that all conditions are satisfied simultaneously.

7.2 OUTPUT PARAMETERS (FAN-OUT)

7.2.1 *A First Approximation Assuming Identical Transistors and Large V_{CC}*

Figure 7.1 is a generalized representation of a *DCTL* NOR gate driving a fan-out of N inverter circuits. Initially, let us assume

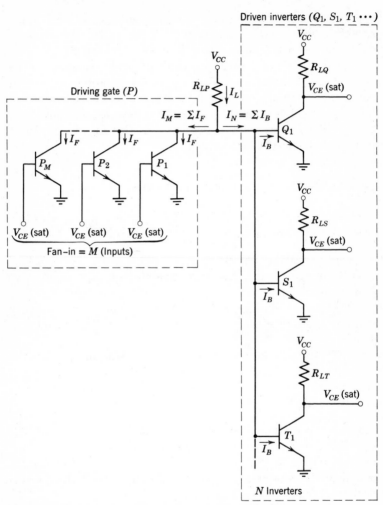

Fig. 7.1. Generalized representation of a *DCTL* NOR gate driving *N* inverters. Voltages are for the gate OFF and the inverters ON.

that *identical npn* silicon transistors with negligible leakage currents are used, and also that V_{CC} is much larger than $V_{CE}(\text{sat})$ and V_{BE}.

If the driving gate, P, is cut off, the collector currents of P_1 through P_M are very small, and for now will be taken as zero. With the circuit in this state, the current I_L through R_{LP} will flow into the bases of the N transistors Q_1, S_1, T_1, . . ., turning them on. To a first approximation, the available drive current I_L is,

$$I_L = \frac{V_{CC}}{R_{LP}} \tag{7.1}$$

It is not sufficient for a *driven* transistor to be merely on. In order to function as a *DCTL* gate, the transistor must enter the region of saturation. This requires that the base current, of say Q_1, be great enough to cause Q_1 to saturate. This requirement can be expressed as

$$I_B(\text{sat}) \geq \frac{I_C(\text{sat})}{\beta_F} = \frac{V_{CC}}{\beta_F R_{LQ}} \tag{7.2}$$

The maximum number of transistors Q_1, S_1, T_1, . . ., which can be driven into saturation by the driving gate P, is called the maximum fan-out of the gate and is usually denoted by $N_{\max}$. Achieving this maximum requires that the *available* drive current I_L in Eq. 7.1 be equal to $N_{\max}$ times the *required* base current $I_B(\text{sat})$ in Eq. 7.2. From the above two equations the maximum fan-out is found to be

$$N_{\max} = \frac{\beta_F R_{LQ}}{R_{LP}} = \beta_F \tag{7.3}$$

for $R_{LP} = R_{LQ}$. This maximum fan-out expression is very optimistic and applies only to the idealized example considered. In practice, a number of additional requirements and limitations may reduce the value of $N_{\max}$ to as little as $\frac{1}{5}$ of this value.

With such a severe practical reduction in fan-out, it might seem reasonable to use transistors with a very high β_F in order to achieve as large a value as possible for fan-out. It turns out, however, that in order to achieve device designs which will exhibit fast switching times, it is necessary to reduce minority-carrier lifetime to a minimum (see Sec. 1.3). This unfortunately has the effect of drastically reducing the beta.

Let us now consider some of the reasons for the great difference between practical fan-out values and the value given in Eq. 7.3.

7.2.2 *Effects of* $V_{CE}(\text{sat})$, V_{BE}, *and Collector OFF Current* (*Identical Transistors*)

When we include the effects of V_{BE} and $V_{CE}(\text{sat})$, we obtain more exact expressions for the currents in Eqs. 7.1 and 7.2.

$$I_L = \frac{V_{CC} - V_{BE}}{R_{LP}} \tag{7.4}$$

$$I_B(\text{sat}) = \frac{1}{\beta_F}\frac{V_{CC} - V_{CE}(\text{sat})}{R_{LQ}} \tag{7.5}$$

There is also a small collector current which flows in each OFF transistor, P_1 through P_M, because of the small forward base-emitter voltage on these transistors [assumed equal to $V_{CE}(\text{sat})$ of a previous ON gate]. This forward bias voltage can be as great as five to ten kT/q. If we denote the OFF-state current as I_F, then, on the basis of the Ebers-Moll equations, Eq. 1.1*b*, we find

$$I_F \cong \alpha_F I_{ES} e^{qV_{CE}(\text{sat})/kT} \tag{7.6}$$

Summing the currents at the junction between the P gate and the other gates, we obtain the basic current equation for fan-out calculations

$$I_L = \sum_1^N I_B + \sum_1^M I_F \tag{7.7}$$

Substituting for the currents from Eqs. 7.4 and 7.5, we obtain for this simple case of identical transistors, and $R_{LQ} = R_{LS} = R_{LT} \ldots$,

$$\frac{V_{CC} - V_{BE}}{R_{LP}} = \frac{N[V_{CC} - V_{CE}(\text{sat})]}{\beta_F R_{LQ}} + MI_F \tag{7.8}$$

Solving Eq. 7.8, we obtain for the maximum fan-out

$$N_{\max} = \beta_F \frac{R_{LQ}}{R_{LP}}\left[\frac{V_{CC} - V_{BE} - MI_F R_{LP}}{V_{CC} - V_{CE}(\text{sat})}\right] \tag{7.9}$$

where I_F is the standby current in each P-gate transistor, as given by Eq. 7.6. Using typical values of $I_{ES} = 10^{-9}$ amp and $V_{CE}(\text{sat}) = 10(kT/q)$, we find that $I_F \cong 20$ μa. Thus, the current MI_F in Eq. 7.9 may become important in low-power circuits.

Typically the bracketed expression in Eq. 7.9 will be of the order of $3/4$, so for $R_{LP} \cong R_{LQ}$, the value of maximum fan-out is reduced to perhaps $(3/4)\beta_F$. There are two principal reasons for the still large difference between this factor and the figure of $\beta_F/5$ which applies to many practical *DCTL* circuits. The first is concerned with base overdrive required for reasons of speed. The second is concerned with "current hogging" in the transistors $Q_1, S_1, T_1, \ldots$, because of unequal V_{BE} characteristics.

7.2.3 *Base Overdrive (Identical Transistors)*

The above relations were based on the assumption that each transistor $Q_1, S_1, T_1, \ldots$, is driven only to the *edge* of saturation. This condition both limits the turn-on speed and, in addition, yields a relatively large value for $V_{CE}(\text{sat})$. This latter effect in turn decreases the voltage margin and hence the noise immunity of the gate, as explained in Sec. 7.3.1. For these reasons, it is desirable to provide additional base current, *over and above* that which is required to merely drive the transistor to the edge of saturation. This base current overdrive causes the transistor to turn on rapidly, and drives it deep into saturation (see Sec. 1.3).

We will define a turn-on overdrive factor n as the ratio of the actual dc base current to the dc base current needed for saturation.

$$n = \frac{I_B}{I_C(\text{sat})/\beta_F} = \frac{I_B R_{LQ}}{V_{CC}} \beta_F \qquad (7.10)$$

If we drive the transistor only to the edge of saturation, then $n = 1$, but if we drive into the saturation region, $n > 1$. Note that this same overdrive factor is used in ECP, Chapter 9, to describe a somewhat different problem—that of the turn-on time of a transistor when driven with a *step* of base current. Since we do not have a step i_B drive here (the i_B waveform is closer to a ramp, see Sec. 2.1.2) the turn-on and turn-off times in the present problem *cannot* be found by application of the formulas involving the overdrive factor in ECP. Basically, however, the so-called turn-on overdrive factor as defined here and in ECP is in fact the ratio of two dc currents, and thus it is appropriate to use the same symbol in both places.

Let us assume, therefore, that the base current to each transistor Q_1, S_1, T_1, . . . , has been increased by the factor n. Accordingly, Eq. 7.9 must be modified as follows.

$$N_{\max} = \frac{\beta_F R_{LQ}}{n R_{LP}} \left[\frac{V_{CC} - V_{BE} - M I_F R_L}{V_{CC} - V_{CE}(\text{sat})} \right] \tag{7.11}$$

Setting the bracketed term equal to $\frac{3}{4}$ as before and using an overdrive factor of $n = 3$ for speed considerations, we obtain for $R_{LQ} = R_{LP}$ the revised value, $N_{\max} = \beta_F/4$. This value now begins to approach that of many practical circuits. For the fastest speeds, it will be necessary to increase the overdrive still further, resulting in an even greater reduction in $N_{\max}$.

7.2.4 Base-Current Hogging (dc Steady State, Nonidentical Transistors)

There is another consideration known as "current hogging" which will reduce the fan-out as given in Eq. 7.9. Current hogging results from the variation in the dc input characteristics among the driven transistors Q_1, S_1, T_1, . . . Nonidentical characteristics will cause the transistor which has the smallest base current for a given V_{BE} to be "current starved" relative to the other transistors, because the latter tend to "hog" the available current. Hence fan-out must be limited to a number such that the transistor with the lowest base current for a given base voltage, V_{BE}, will still be driven into saturation.

Figure 7.2b shows an idealized base-emitter characteristic which results when the circuit in Fig. 7.2a is driven from cut-off into saturation. This characteristic can be explained on the basis of the Ebers-Moll equation for the base current of an npn transistor:

$$I_B = I_{ES}(1 - \alpha_F)(e^{qV_{BE}/kT} - 1) + I_{CS}(1 - \alpha_R)(e^{-qV_{CB}/kT} - 1) \tag{7.12}$$

If $(1 - \alpha_R) \gg (1 - \alpha_F)$, a sharp break in the base current characteristics will occur at the point where the collector-base junction becomes forward biased, because the second term in Eq. 7.12 will rapidly become dominant for $-V_{CB} > kT/q$.

Figure 7.2b shows the input characteristic which results when two quite different transistors are used in the circuit in Fig. 7.2a.

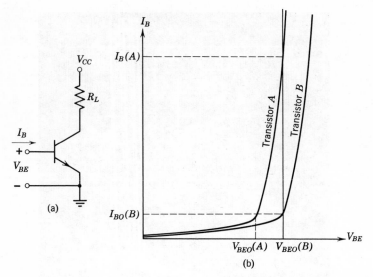

Fig. 7.2. Idealized V_{BE} vs. I_B characteristics of a simple transistor circuit driven into saturation. (a) Circuit. (b) Input characteristics of two different transistors A and B.

It is clear from Eq. 7.12 that such differences arise from differences in the saturation currents and/or alphas of the two transistors. (Remember, however, that this characteristic is also a function of R_L and V_{CC}, which we have considered fixed in this measurement.)

It is clear from Fig. 7.2 that if both transistors are driven with the same base voltage V_{BE}, transistor A will be deep in saturation and drawing a large base current when transistor B is just barely saturated. It is convenient to represent the ratio of base currents under these conditions by a parameter ϵ, defined as

$$\epsilon = \frac{I_B(A)}{I_{BO}(B)}\bigg|_{V_{BE} = V_{BEO}(B)} \tag{7.13}$$

That is, ϵ is measured with transistor B barely saturated. Clearly $\epsilon \geq 1$.

If we now consider that the N driven transistors in Fig. 7.1 may be nonuniform as in Fig. 7.2, a little thought will show that the most severe limitation on the fan-out occurs when there is *one* starved transistor operating with a base voltage $V_{BEO}(B)$ and a

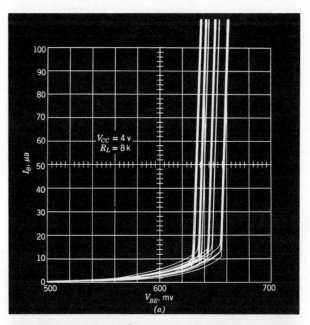

(a)

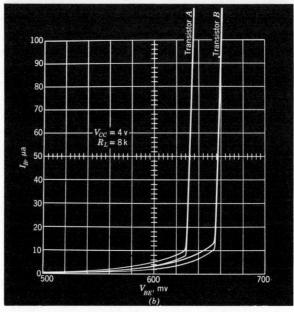

(b)

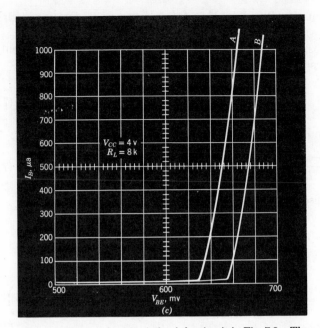

Fig. 7.3. Measured input characteristic of the circuit in Fig. 7.2a. The voltage zero has been suppressed to give greater resolution. The technique is described in TCH, Chapter 7. (a) Characteristic for ten randomly selected silicon transistors. (b) Characteristic of the two extremes in (a). (c) Same transistors as in (b), plotted over a wider current scale.

In this and subsequent oscilloscope photographs, substantial hysteresis is visible in the curves. This effect, which arises from capacitive effects (see TCH, Chapter 7) is particularly pronounced when the curve tracer is used at very high sensitivity. The average of the two hysteresis lines should be used when numerical values are to be read from the curves.

current $I_{BO}(B)$ while $N - 1$ transistors are operating with the same voltage, and a current $I_B(A) = \epsilon I_{BO}(B)$.

Substituting these parameters in the basic fan-out current relationship for Fig. 7.1

$$I_L = \sum_1^N I_B + \sum_1^M I_F \qquad (7.14)$$

we find that

$$\frac{V_{CC} - V_{BEO}(B)}{R_{LP}} = I_{BO}(B) + (N - 1)\epsilon I_{BO}(B) + MI_F \qquad (7.15)$$

Because transistor B is just barely saturated,

$$\beta_F(B)I_{BO}(B) = I_C(\text{sat}) = \frac{V_{CC} - V_{CE}(\text{sat})}{R_{LQ}}$$

On this basis we obtain for the maximum fan-out

$$N_{\max} = \frac{\beta_F(B)R_{LQ}}{\epsilon R_{LP}}\left[\frac{V_{CC} - V_{BEO}(B) - MI_F R_{LP}}{V_{CC} - V_{CE}(\text{sat})}\right] + \left(1 - \frac{1}{\epsilon}\right) \qquad (7.16)$$

Figure 7.3a is a photograph of the input characteristics of the circuit in Fig. 7.2a, using a group of ten randomly selected 2N708 transistors. The two extreme members of this group of curves are replotted in Figs. 7.3b and c with different vertical scales so that ϵ can be calculated. For this example it appears that $\epsilon \approx 70$. It is clear from Eq. 7.16 that if transistors with such a wide spread in characteristics were used, an enormous reduction in fan-out would result.

7.2.5 *Base Padding Resistance (Nonidentical Transistors)*

An obvious method of reducing the current-hogging effect is to use a padding resistor R_B in series with each base to equalize the base currents. Figure 7.4 shows the effect of adding a base resistor to the same two transistors A and B shown in Figs. 7.3b and c. It is clear that the slope of the characteristic in the saturation region is greatly reduced as R_B is increased, thus drastically reducing ϵ. Figure 7.5 shows ϵ plotted as a function of R_B. In practice, it is common to find fairly fast switching *DCTL* gates which

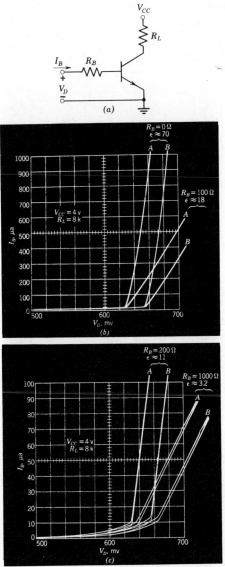

Fig. 7.4. Effect of adding series base resistance. (*a*) Circuit. (*b*) Measured input characteristic (I_B versus the driving voltage V_D) for the circuit in (*a*), using transistors *A* and *B* of Figs. 7.3*b* and *c*. (*c*) Measured input characteristic, but with larger values of R_B. Note the change in current scale.

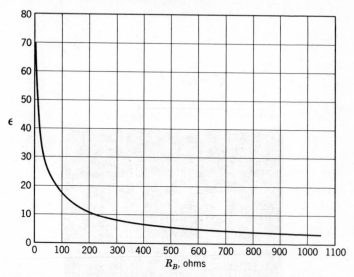

Fig. 7.5. Plot of ϵ vs. R_B obtained from the curves in Fig. 7.4.

use values for the padding resistance, R_B, of the order of 1 k, which, for the particular transistors considered here, gives a value of $\epsilon \approx 3$.

The circuit for the NOR gate with bast resistors included is shown in Fig. 7.6. The addition of base padding resistors somewhat complicates the fan-out calculation because the inverters no longer have identical base voltages. If we designate the voltage at the central node as V_D, then for transistor Q_1 we have

$$V_D = V_{BE}(Q_1) + I_B(Q_1)R_B \qquad (7.17)$$

A similar expression holds for transistors S_1, T_1, ... Summing the currents at node V_D (i.e., Eq. 7.7), we obtain

$$\frac{V_{CC} - V_D}{R_{LP}} = \sum_1^N I_B + MI_F \qquad (7.18)$$

Because the relation between V_{BE} and I_B is nonlinear, Eqs. 7.17 and 7.18 are difficult to solve by other than graphical methods. A graphical approach is particularly simple if we settle at this point for the worst-case solution for N, rather than the general solution. Specifically, we can find from a load-line construction on a representative set of input characteristics which transistor will be most

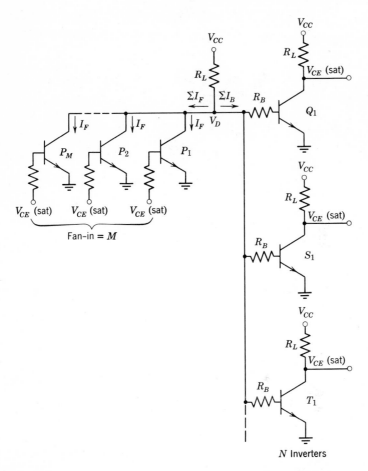

Fig. 7.6. Circuit arrangement for *DCTL* NOR gate with base padding resistors. Voltages are for P off, Q_1, S_1, T_1 on.

difficult to saturate. (Because of the presence of R_B, this will not necessarily be the transistor with the highest V_{BEO}, as was the case in Sec. 7.2.4.) We can also find from the graph the highest base current required, and hence the current ratio ϵ.

Figure 7.7b shows a hypothetical scatter plot of the input characteristics for the circuit in 7.7a. The location of the point of saturation for each transistor is indicated by a small circle. Equa-

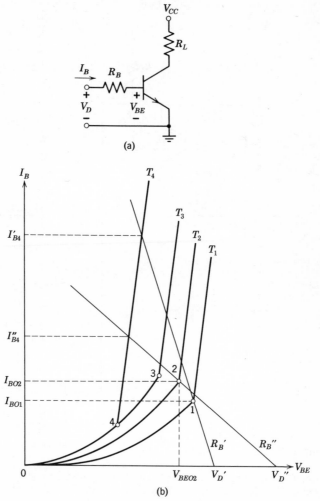

Fig. 7.7. Graphical construction to find worst-case transistor. (*a*) Circuit. (*b*) Hypothetical scatter plot of the input characteristics I_B vs. V_{BE} for the circuit in (*a*).

tion 7.17 has been plotted as a "load line" on the characteristics for two possible choices of resistor R_B, designated as R_B' and R_B''. The basic worst-case requirement is that the "worst" transistor be just saturated, and all other transistors be driven well into saturation. Thus the load line must be located so that all of the points of saturation are *below* the load line. For example, if all transistors have base padding resistors of value R_B', then the load line for R_B' is drawn through the saturation point 1 to insure that transistor T_1 is just saturated, and all other transistors are well saturated. In this case $\epsilon' = I_{B4}'/I_{BO1}$. If this value of ϵ is still too large, then the base resistor might be increased to a value R_B''. We then discover that transistor T_2 determines the positioning of the load line, and the new current ratio becomes $\epsilon'' = I_{B4}''/I_{BO2}$. (Note that this load-line calculation of ϵ is equivalent to finding ϵ from a plot of I_B vs. V_D, as in Fig. 7.4. However, Fig. 7.7 is more useful for this calculation because the nonlinear characteristic does not have to be replotted for each different value of R_B.)

We can now use these graphically derived values to solve Eqs. 7.17 and 7.18 for the fan-out. To be specific, let us assume that ϵ'' as calculated above represents a "reasonable" current ratio (i.e., *much* smaller than $\epsilon = 70$ with which we started). The worst-case of input characteristic distribution for $R_B = R_B''$ would result if one transistor were like T_2 and all others were like T_4. On this basis, Eq. 7.18 becomes

$$\frac{V_{CC} - V_D''}{R_{LP}} = I_{BO2} + (N - 1)\epsilon''I_{BO2} + MI_F$$

This equation together with Eq. 7.17 and the relation for the base current in T_2 at the edge of saturation

$$I_{BO2} = \frac{V_{CC} - V_{CE}(\text{sat})}{\beta_{F2}R_{L2}}$$

can be solved to yield the desired expression for maximum fan-out:

$$N_{\max} = \frac{\beta_{F2}R_{L2}}{\epsilon''R_{LP}}\left[\frac{V_{CC} - V_{BEO2} - MI_FR_{LP}}{V_{CC} - V_{CE}(\text{sat})}\right] + \left(1 - \frac{1}{\epsilon''}\right) - \frac{1}{\epsilon''}\frac{R_B''}{R_{LP}}$$

$$(7.19)$$

Note that *specific* values of some of the parameters, i.e., β_{F2}, R_B'' R_{L2}, V_{BEO2}, and ϵ'', appear in this equation, because we have already taken the worst case of current hogging by means of the graphical analysis in Fig. 7.7. In completing the worst-case analysis for N, these parameters should *not* be changed; only the remaining parameters should be adjusted for worst-case conditions. As a specific illustration of this point, it is clear from Fig. 7.7 that β_{F2} is *not* the smallest β_F of this group, even though a "conventional" worst-case analysis of Eq. 7.19 would clearly call for $\beta_F = \beta_F(\min)$. (This general comment also applies to Eq. 7.16.)

Equation 7.19 provides some guidance for choosing a suitable value of R_B. As R_B is increased, ϵ decreases (see Figs. 7.4, 7.5, and 7.6) and $N_{\max}$ will initially increase since the first term in Eq. 7.19 will be dominant. However, for large values of R_B, ϵ will approach 1 while the last term of Eq. 7.19 will dominate and will ultimately reduce the fan-out to zero (we can no longer obtain enough current to saturate the transistors). Since in order to be useful as a *DCTL* gate, a fan-out of at least $N = 2$ is normally required, it is apparent that an upper limit on R_B exists (see Problems P7.1 and P7.2).

7.2.6 *Base Overdrive (Non-identical Transistors)*

In Sec. 7.2.3 we studied the influence of switching speed on fan-out. Because in that section we assumed that all transistors were identical, useful answers could be obtained in terms of a steady-state overdrive factor n. In Sec. 7.2.4 and 7.2.5 we calculated the effect of nonidentical transistors on gate performance *neglecting* the switching speed issue, requiring only that in the steady state all transistors be saturated. The solution involved the *static* nonlinear input characteristics of the circuit.

The next logical step in the development is to calculate the fan-out with nonidentical transistors *and overdrive* to obtain fast switching. Unfortunately, this is a nonlinear dynamic problem which is of sufficient complexity to be beyond the scope of this text. It is a relatively simple matter, however, to modify the results of Sec. 7.2.3 (*identical* transistors) to include in the overdrive calculations the effect of the base padding resistors (see Problem P7.3).

7.3 VOLTAGE MARGIN

7.3.1 *Specification of Voltage Margin*

As mentioned in the introduction, the dc operating bias requirement for the *DCTL* circuit configuration shown in Fig. 7.1

is that the collector saturation voltage $V_{CE}(\text{sat})$ be less than the base-to-emitter voltage necessary to turn the following transistor on. The difference between these two voltages represents the voltage margin Δ,

$$\Delta = V_{BE} - V_{CE}(\text{sat}) \tag{7.20}$$

and is a value which a noise voltage must exceed in order to cause a spurious transition from one state to the other.

To focus the discussion on the specific issue of voltage margin, let us consider in detail a simple *DCTL* circuit of three cascaded inverters, as shown in Fig. 7.8a. Figure 7.8b shows the "voltage band" picture for the dc voltage transfer characteristics of the P inverter in this cascade. When the input voltage to transistor P is less than the threshold voltage V_{BET}, transistor P is off, and the output voltage V_D is equal to $V_{BE}(\text{sat})$, the base-to-emitter voltage of the saturated driven transistor Q, as shown in Fig. 7.8b. On the other hand, when the input voltage to transistor P is greater than V_{BEO}, then transistor P is saturated, and the output voltage V_D falls to $V_{CE}(\text{sat})$.

The voltage margin of the circuit in Fig. 7.8a can be found by assuming that transistor K is saturated, and calculating how large a noise voltage e_n can be tolerated before unsatisfactory performance results. With transistor K saturated, $V_{CE}(K) = V_{CE}(\text{sat})$, and transistor P is supposed to be off. If we specify that transistor P must *never become saturated* under these conditions, then from Fig. 7.8b the noise voltage e_n must never be greater than $V_{BEO} - V_{CE}(\text{sat})$, or the voltage margin is

$$\Delta_O = V_{BEO} - V_{CE}(\text{sat}) \tag{7.21}$$

If we establish a more conservative criterion by specifying that transistor P must *never enter the active region* when transistor K is saturated, then from Fig. 7.8b the voltage margin becomes

$$\Delta_T = V_{BET} - V_{CE}(\text{sat}) \tag{7.22}$$

Actually, a realistic definition of voltage margin lies somewhere between the two extremes given by Eqs. 7.21 and 7.22. To see this, let us examine the circuit in Fig. 7.8a in more detail. If transistor K is on, transistor P should be off, and transistor Q on. However, we really do not care about the precise state of P, as long as Q is indeed on, because the output representation will be in terms of the

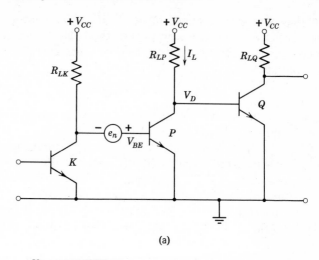

(a)

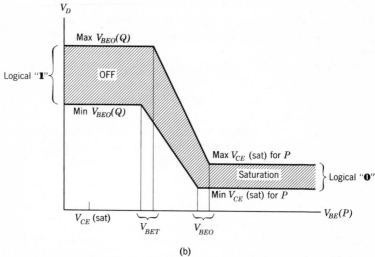

(b)

Fig. 7.8. Voltage margin. (*a*) Elementary DCTL circuit: three cascaded inverters. (*b*) Idealized *DCTL* voltage transfer characteristics of transistor *P* showing the "band" concept of the voltage margin.

state of Q. Thus the required circuit condition can be stated in terms of the base voltage or base current of the Q transistor at the edge of saturation:

$$I_B(Q) \geqslant I_{BO} \qquad (7.23)$$

or

$$V_{BE}(Q) \geqslant V_{BEO} \qquad (7.24)$$

To relate these inequalities back to $V_{BE}(P)$, we must sum currents at the V_D node. The current through R_{LP} is

$$I_L = \frac{V_{CC} - V_D}{R_{LP}} \qquad (7.25a)$$

$$= \frac{V_{CC} - V_{BE}(Q)}{R_{LP}} \qquad (7.25b)$$

and the collector current of transistor P is, from Eq. 1.1,

$$I_C(P) \cong \alpha_F I_{ES} e^{q V_{BE}(P)/kT} \qquad (7.26)$$

Summing currents at the V_D node and solving for $V_{BE}(P)$, we obtain

$$V_{BE}(P) = \frac{kT}{q} \ln \left[\frac{V_{CC} - V_{BE}(Q) - R_{LP} I_B(Q)}{\alpha_F I_{ES} R_{LP}} \right] \qquad (7.27)$$

Substituting for V_{BE} and I_B from Eqs. 7.23 and 7.24, we obtain an inequality in terms of the *limiting value* V_{BEL} for the base-to-emitter voltage of transistor P.

$$V_{BE}(P) \leqslant V_{BEL} = \frac{kT}{q} \ell \mathrm{n} \left[\frac{V_{CC} - V_{BEO} - R_{LP} I_{BO}}{\alpha_F I_{ES} R_{LP}} \right] \qquad (7.28)$$

Thus to insure that the circuit always meets the conditions specified in Eqs. 7.23 and 7.24, the noise voltage e_n must always be less than $V_{BEL} - V_{CE}(\text{sat})$. That is, the voltage margin is

$$\Delta_L = V_{BEL} - V_{CE}(\text{sat}) \qquad (7.29)$$

A little thought will show that V_{BEL} always lies between V_{BEO} and V_{BET}, and thus the voltage margin calculated from Eq. 7.29 will be intermediate between the values calculated from Eq. 7.21 and Eq. 7.22.

To find the worst-case Δ_L, we choose the maximum $V_{CE}(\text{sat})$ for the transistors in question, and the minimum V_{BEL}. On the basis of Eq. 7.28, this latter condition implies choosing the minimum V_{CC} and the maximum α_F, I_{ES}, and R_{LP}. However, because of the nonlinear relationship between V_{BEO} and I_{BO}, it is not obvious which transistor possesses the worst-case combination of these latter parameters. The problem is clearly very similar to that discussed in Sec. 7.2.5, and thus we again resort to a graphical solution. Figure 7.9 shows a hypothetical spread of I_{BO}, V_{BEO} values for a number of transistors. To find the worst-case Δ, it is clear from Eq. 7.28 that the maximum value of the sum $(V_{BEO} + I_{BO}R_{LP})$ should be used, and this can be readily determined by drawing the R_{LP} load line such that all of the V_{BEO}, I_{BO} points fall either on or below the line as shown in Fig. 7.9. This construction identifies the worst-case transistor and hence the worst-case V_{BEO}, I_{BO} combination for use in Eq. 7.28.

If, for the reasons discussed in Secs. 7.2.4 and 7.2.5, base padding resistors have been included in the circuit as in Fig. 7.10, then the determination of the voltage margin is not quite so direct, because

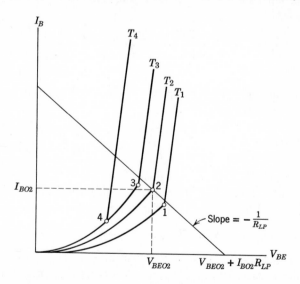

Fig. 7.9. Load-line construction for finding the worst-case V_{BEO} and I_{BO} combination.

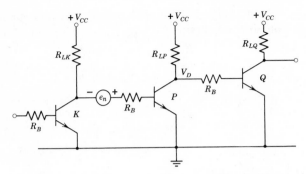

Fig. 7.10. *DCTL* inverters with base padding resistors.

V_D is now no longer equal to the base voltage of transistor Q. In this case,

$$V_D = V_{BE}(Q) + R_B I_B(Q) \qquad (7.30)$$

Substituting this expression for V_D into Eq. 7.25a, and summing the currents and solving as before, we obtain a relation for the limiting base voltage when base-padding resistors are used:

$$V_{BE}(P) < V_{BEL} = \frac{kT}{q} \ln \left[\frac{V_{CC} - V_{BEO} - (R_B + R_{LP})I_{BO}}{\alpha_F I_{ES} R_{LP}} \right]$$

$$(7.31)$$

The voltage margin expression (Eq. 7.29) remains unchanged. A construction similar to that shown in Fig. 7.9 can again be used to find the worst-case V_{BEL}, except now the load line is determined by $R_B + R_{LP}$.

Having developed the basic equations for calculating voltage margin, we examine in the following sections the expressions for the transistor voltages $V_{CE}(\text{sat})$, V_{BET}, and V_{BEO}, which are of importance in calculating Δ.

7.3.2 *Collector Saturation Voltage $V_{CE}(sat)$*

An expression for the collector saturation voltage in terms of I_C and I_B has already been developed in Chapter 1 (see Eq. 1.9b). This equation can be somewhat simplified by writing the expression in terms of the overdrive factor, n. Substituting $I_C(\text{sat})/I_B = \beta_F/n$

into Eq. 1.9*b*, and changing the polarity to that appropriate for an *npn* transistor, we obtain

$$V_{CE}(\text{sat}) = \frac{kT}{q}\ln\frac{1}{\alpha_R} + \frac{kT}{q}\ln\frac{n+a}{n-1} \qquad (7.32)$$

where *a* is defined as

$$a = \beta_F(1 - \alpha_R)$$

The minimum value of $V_{CE}(\text{sat})$, corresponding to large overdrive, is, from Eq. 7.32,

$$V_{CE}(\text{sat}) = \frac{kT}{q}\ln\frac{1}{\alpha_R} \qquad (7.33)$$

Figure 7.11 is a graph of Eq. 7.32 for a transistor with $\beta_F = 30$. Many present-day switching transistors have values for α_R ranging from 0.1 to 0.5. So-called "chopper" and symmetrical transistors, designed for unusually low offset-voltage, may have values for

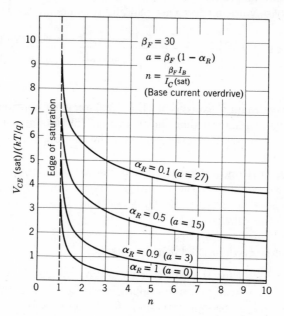

Fig. 7.11. $V_{CE}(\text{sat})$ vs. base overdrive, *n*.

α_R as high as 0.9, but the switching speed of these is generally much lower than transistors designed for use in logic gates.

Manufacturers generally show curves of the collector saturation voltage either versus I_B or versus I_C with the other current as a parameter. A typical manufacturers' curve is shown in Fig. 7.12. The dashed curve represents the contour for a constant I_C/I_B. From this dashed curve it is apparent that there are effects which are not included in Eq. 7.32. The principal additional effects involve the voltage drops across the collector and emitter body and lead resistances, and the variation in β_F with the drive level. No simple analytical expressions are available for these effects, so we must rely on experimental data.

7.3.3 *Base-Emitter Threshold Voltage,* V_{BET}

The base-to-emitter threshold voltage was defined in Chapter 6 as the voltage at which the transistor just begins to conduct. Since the $V_{BE} - I_B$ characteristic is exponential, there is no unique value which can be called *the* threshold voltage. However, because the collector current increases so rapidly with V_{BE}, we may define V_{BET} as that value of V_{BE} which permits a negligible collector current I_{CT} (relative to the normal operating current) to flow. That is, for V_{BE} equal to V_{BET},

$$I_C = I_{CT} = \gamma I_C(\text{sat}) \tag{7.34}$$

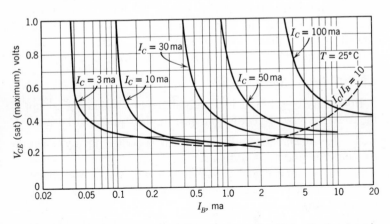

Fig. 7.12. Maximum $V_{CE}(\text{sat})$ vs. base current, I_B. Note the increase in $V_{CE}(\text{sat})$ with large base current drive, for constant $I_C/I_B = 10$ (dashed curve).

where $\gamma \ll 1$. From the Ebers-Moll equations (Eq. 1.1) we find that for an *npn* transistor in the active region, the base voltage is related to I_C by the relation

$$V_{BE} \cong \frac{kT}{q} \ln \left[\frac{I_C}{\alpha_F I_{ES}} \right] \qquad (7.35)$$

Substituting from Eq. 7.34, we obtain a definition of the threshold voltage for an *npn* transistor

$$V_{BET} \cong \frac{kT}{q} \ln \left[\frac{\gamma I_C(\text{sat})}{\alpha_F I_{ES}} \right] \qquad (7.36)$$

It is clear from Eq. 7.36 that V_{BET} is not uniquely a parameter of the transistor, because $I_C(\text{sat})$ is circuit-dependent.

7.3.4 *Base Voltage at the Edge of Saturation*, V_{BEO}

The voltage V_{BEO}, defined as the base-to-emitter voltage at the edge of saturation, is also a circuit-dependent parameter, and for this reason is not normally specified in manufacturers' literature. However, it is possible to estimate V_{BEO} from the published values of $V_{BE}(\text{sat})$, the base-emitter voltage for the condition of the transistor operating in the saturation region. Curves for this latter quantity are usually given for a fixed circuit current ratio $I_C/I_B = 10$ as shown in Fig. 7.13. The value of $V_{BE}(\text{sat})$ will be 10 to 50 mv larger than V_{BEO}, because the latter is measured at the edge of saturation. Curves for $V_{CE}(\text{sat})$ have also been included in Fig. 7.13, so that the figure can be used to estimate the voltage margin from either Eq. 7.21 or Eq. 7.29.

7.3.5 *Noise in Digital Circuits*

Noise may be generated in many different ways in digital equipment. Noise may originate from outside the equipment because of:

(1) electromagnetic radiation which is picked up by a circuit conductor acting as an antenna,

(2) power supply and power line noise from other operating equipment, such as rotating machinery or equipment with electrical contactors.

These outside sources may be partially suppressed by shielding and filtering.

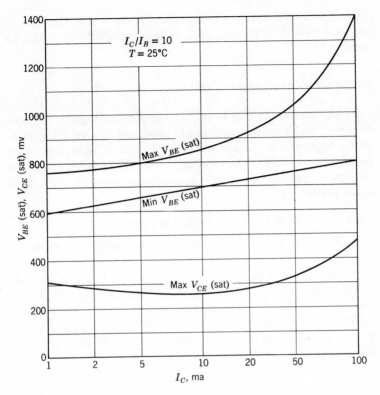

Fig. 7.13. Saturation voltage limits for a silicon transistor.

Noise may also originate within the digital equipment itself. Logic noise can be generated by fast switching of high currents on ground return busses, particularly between logic cards. The resulting voltage drops developed across lead inductances can be amplified and propagated, causing false state transitions in gates and triggering of flip-flops.

Perhaps the most effective means of reducing logic noise due to the above effects is to use an extended ground plane to which all the circuits are connected with the shortest possible leads. Such a system, because it reduces both lead inductance and skin effect, can reduce logic noise spikes to as little as one-tenth that which would be obtained with conventional wiring. It is necessary, of course, to consider also the total cross-sectional area of any conductor used as a common return path to make sure that the dc and low-frequency voltage drop is low enough for the circuits employed.

7.4 INPUT PARAMETERS (FAN-IN)

Ideally one would like to be able to connect together the collectors of an unlimited number of transistors in a *DCTL* gate to obtain unlimited fan-in, but just as in the case of fan-out, practical limits arise which limit the value of M. In a *DCTL* NOR gate, these limitations usually arise either from voltage-margin limitations or speed limitations.

7.4.1 *Influence of Fan-in on Voltage Margin*

To illustrate the influence of fan-in on voltage margin, we modify the circuit in Fig. 7.8a by replacing transistor P with a NOR gate, as shown in Fig. 7.14. As in Sec. 7.3.1, we wish to calculate the voltage margin at the input to P_1 when transistor K is on, and all transistors in the P gate are supposed to be off. The voltages indicated in the figure apply for this circuit condition. For simplicity we shall deal here only with the relatively simple voltage-margin criterion

$$\Delta_O = V_{BEO} - V_{CE}(\text{sat}) \qquad (7.37)$$

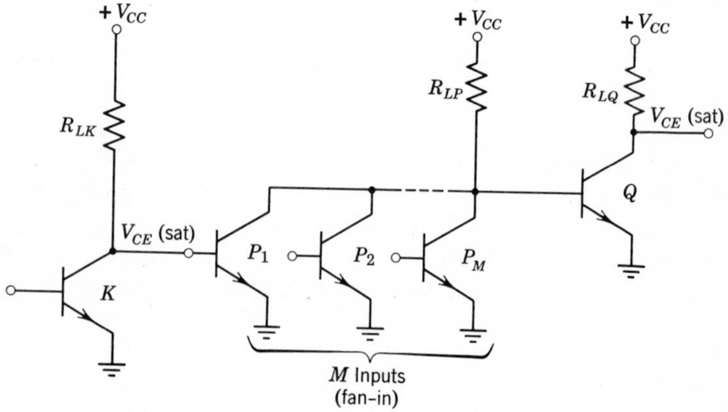

Fig. 7.14. Inverter — NOR gate — inverter combination.

(The discussion can be extended readily to include the more realistic criterion of Eqs. 7.28 and 7.29; see Problem P7.4.) Thus we wish to examine the variation of the voltage V_{BEO} for transistor P_1 as the fan-in M is changed.

To this end, let us examine the input characteristics of transistor P_1 in the NOR gate of Fig. 7.14, assuming that the inputs of all the transistors $P_1 \ldots P_M$ are driven with identical waveforms. As M is increased, the collector current of transistor P_1 will be decreased and the input characteristic curve of P_1 will be modified. Figure 7.15 shows the input characteristics for a silicon transistor when used in a NOR gate with a fan-in of $M = 1, 2, 5$ or 10. The effect on the base voltage V_{BEO} is clearly shown: the knee of the curve is displaced to the left and hence V_{BEO} is decreased as the number of input transistors is increased. This decrease can be explained as follows. When all of the transistors in the P gate in Fig. 7.14 are at the edge of saturation, the collector current in each transistor will be

$$I_C(\text{sat}) = \frac{1}{M} \left[\frac{V_{CC} - V_{CE}(\text{sat})}{R_L} \right] \tag{7.38}$$

Thus the collector current in each saturated transistor is reduced as M is increased. The base current at the edge of saturation is by definition

$$I_{BO} = \frac{I_C(\text{sat})}{\beta_F} \tag{7.39}$$

Thus I_{BO} will also decrease as M increases, and it follows from the exponential relationship between I_{BO} and V_{BEO} that V_{BEO} must also decrease.

It is clear from the above discussion, and particularly from Fig. 7.15, that the voltage margin Δ_O (in this case the Δ appropriate to the input of the P gate) will decrease as M is increased.

The voltage margin also changes because of the dependence of $V_{CE}(\text{sat})$ on M, but this effect is usually small compared to the change in V_{BEO} with M discussed above.

7.4.2 *Influence of Fan-in on Switching Speed*

The reduction in collector current with increasing M (Eq. 7.38) will decrease the switching speed of the transistor, an effect which

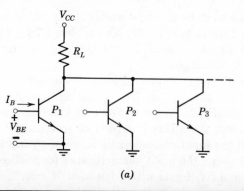

(a)

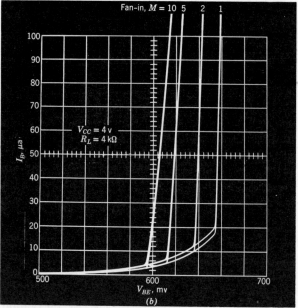

(b)

Fig. 7.15. The effect of fan-in, M, on the base-emitter voltage at saturation, V_{BEO}. (a) Circuit for measurement. $P_2, P_3 \ldots$ have base drives identical to that of P_1. (b) Measured curves. For details of measurement, see TCM, Chapter 7.

may become quite significant for larger values of M. Assuming that the base drive to a transistor in the P gate remains constant, the decrease in collector current will result in *increased* overdrive. This will decrease the turn-on time somewhat, but will greatly *increase* the turn-off time because of excessive minority carrier storage in the base region and because there is no corresponding *turn-off overdrive* for the circuit we are considering.

7.4.3 *Input Characteristic for a Saturated Gate (Identical Transistors)*

When a NOR gate is used to directly drive other NOR gates, as will be discussed in Sec. 7.5, we must know the input characteristic of one transistor in a gate when the other M-1 transistors in that gate are saturated. Specifically, we wish to measure the input characteristics of, say, transistor P_1 in Fig. 7.16a when all transistors in the P gate, except for P_1, are on.

The results of this measurement are shown in Fig. 7.16b. Included for reference are two curves for fixed collector voltage, $V_{CE} = 0$ and $V_{CE} = +4$ volts. The central four curves show the input characteristic of P_1 as $M - 1$ *saturated* transistors are connected to the gate ($M = 1, 2, 5,$ and 10). The $M = 1$ curve is for the transistor P_1 alone and thus exhibits the sharp break as it enters saturation as has been explained in Sec. 7.2.4. For M greater than one, V_{CE} for P_1 is held nearly constant at a low voltage because the other $M - 1$ transistors are saturated. Thus, the characteristics for this circuit closely resemble those of a single transistor plotted with a low fixed collector voltage (see, for example, ECP, Fig. 2.21).

The knee in the $M = 1$ curve (corresponding to the edge of saturation) is not visible for $M > 1$ because the collector voltage is now held at such a low voltage by the other saturated transistors that saturation in transistor P_1 occurs at a very low value of V_{BE}, say 0.1 volts. Since the zero of these curves has been suppressed, such a knee would be out of the picture on the left.

The leftward displacement of the input characteristic curve for P_1 with increasing M will affect the fan-out of any driving transistor connected to the input of P_1. This is one of the interactions between input and output parameters which was referred to earlier, and will be discussed in the next section. This displacement can also affect the voltage margin under certain specialized conditions.

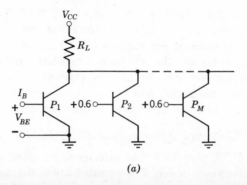

(a)

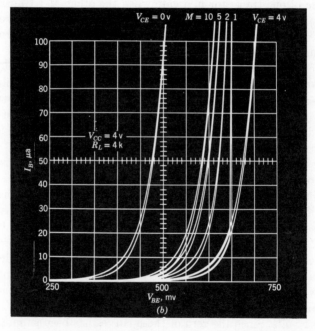

(b)

Fig. 7.16. Input characteristics for one gate input in a *DCTL* NOR gate whose other *M*-1 transistors remain ON. Two reference curves for $V_{CE} = 0$ volts and $V_{CE} = 4$ volts are also shown. (a) Circuit. (b) Input characteristics of the circuit in (a).

7.5 FAN-OUT FOR A NOR GATE DRIVING OTHER NOR GATES
(Identical Transistors)

Up to this point we have discussed the fan-in, fan-out, and voltage margin in terms of a NOR gate loaded with N transistor inverters. One inverter is something termed a "standard" load, since its input represents a reasonably simple and predictable characteristic (assuming that a base-padding resistor is used). Inverter circuits are often used on gate outputs to provide isolation and driving capability, and hence the calculations in preceding sections represent a useful description of practical circuits.

However, in the interest of simplicity, economy, and speed, one frequently uses NOR gates to directly drive other NOR gates. Figure 7.17 shows this circuit arrangement. This circuit raises the issue of interaction between fan-in and fan-out, because the fan-out load which the P gate must drive is now dependent on the fan-in characteristics of the *driven* gates.

For calculating the worst case of fan-out of the P gate in Fig. 7.17, it is clear that all transistors in the P gate should be in the OFF state, thus forcing transistors Q_1, S_1, T_1, . . . to be on. However, the worst-case state of transistors Q_2, Q_3, . . ., S_2, S_3, . . . is not immediately obvious. For this reason we shall discuss two possible states of these transistors in the following subsections. One thing is clear, however. On the basis of Secs. 7.4.1 and 7.4.3, there will be a serious current-hogging problem with this circuit, even for the case of identical transistors assumed here. Specifically, it can be seen from Figs. 7.15 and 7.16 that the input characteristic of one transistor in a NOR gate is a function of the fan-in of that gate. Thus, when the driven gates are not in identical states, or do not have identical fan-in, i.e., $M_Q \neq M_S$, there will be current hogging just as there was when we tried to drive inverters which had nonidentical input characteristics (Secs. 7.2.4 and 7.2.5). To reduce the current-hogging, we have included in Fig. 7.17 base padding resistors, as suggested in Sec. 7.2.5.

7.5.1 *Fan-Out for Driven Gates Saturated*

One possible worst-case state for fan-out in Fig. 7.17 is as follows.

(1) The driving P gate is off.
(2) Only transistor Q_1 is on in the Q gate.

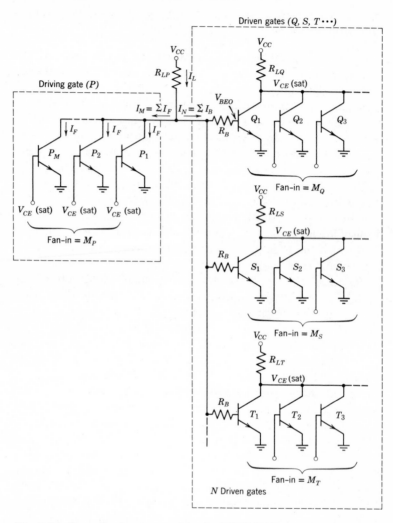

Fig. 7.17. Generalized representation of a *DCTL* NOR gate driving N other similar gates. Voltages are for the P gate off and the other gates on.

(3) All the other driven gates S, T, . . . are on and saturated with at least S_2, T_2, . . . on in addition to S_1, T_1 . . . .

The appropriate input characteristics for calculating the current-hogging factor ϵ for this condition are shown in Fig. 7.16. Unlike the calculation in Sec. 7.2.5 (or, more specifically, Fig. 7.7), there is no ambiguity here about which transistor is hardest to drive. In this case the transistor in the gate with only one transistor on (i.e., Q_1 for these assumed states) will be starved. It is clear from Fig. 7.16 that the worst-case state for gates S, T, . . . is to have all transistors on. Under these assumed conditions we would obtain, by drawing an R_B load line on Fig. 7.16, a value for ϵ. The fan-out expression would then be (from Eq. 7.19):

$$N = \frac{\beta_F(Q)R_{LQ}}{\epsilon R_{LP}} \left[\frac{V_{CC} - V_{BEO}(Q) - M_P I_F R_{LP}}{V_{CC} - V_{CE}(\text{sat})} \right]$$
$$+ 1 - \frac{1}{\epsilon}\left(1 + \frac{R_B}{R_{LP}}\right) \quad (7.40)$$

This expression can be extended to include the effects of nonidentical transistors by using the concepts in Sec. 7.2.5.

7.5.2 *Fan-Out when Driven Gates Have Identical Base Drives*

A second possible worst-case condition for fan-out in Fig. 7.17 would occur if:

(1) The driving P gate is off.
(2) Only transistor Q_1 in the Q gate is being driven, i.e., Q_2, Q_3 . . . off.
(3) All other transistors S_2, S_3, T_2, T_3, . . . in the driven gates are being driven by other gates with a waveform identical to that driving Q_1, S_1, T_1, . . .

The input characteristics appropriate for calculating ϵ in this case are shown in Fig. 7.15. A little thought will show, however, that this condition with identical base drives will always yield a smaller value of ϵ (for a given base padding resistor) than the case with S_2, S_3, T_2, T_3 . . . all saturated, as discussed in the preceding section. Comparison of Fig. 7.15 with Fig. 7.16 will bear this out. For this reason the case with identical base drives will never be the worst case.

7.6 TEMPERATURE EFFECTS

The principal effects of temperature on the operation of *DCTL* circuits is the change in the voltage margin which results from the temperature coefficients of V_{BE} and $V_{CE}(\text{sat})$, and the change in fan-out as a result of the temperature coefficient of β_F. Manufacturers' curves for the variation of $V_{BE}(\text{sat})$ and $V_{CE}(\text{sat})$ with temperature are shown in Figs. 1.5 and 1.6 respectively. These curves indicate that there is a significant decrease in voltage margin as the temperature increases.

The maximum fan-in and maximum fan-out tend to *increase* with increased temperature because both are directly related to β_F, which increases with temperature as shown in Fig. 1.7. As a result, it is at the lowest operating temperatures that the worst-case values of fan-in and fan-out should be determined (if leakage effects can be neglected).

Another important thermal effect results from the familiar rapid increase in collector leakage current with temperature (Fig. 1.4). At elevated temperatures, this increase can cause a serious deterioration in maximum fan-out. For germanium transistors at elevated temperatures the *decrease* in fan-out because of collector leakage may exceed the *increase* because of increased beta.

PROBLEMS

P7.1 Starting from Eq. 7.19 determine the equation for fan-out for large values of R_B/R_{LP} (ϵ approaching unity).

P7.2 Starting from Eq. 7.19 determine the limit on R_B/R_{LP} for a minimum fan-out of $N = 2$.

P7.3 For the circuit in Fig. 7.1, modified by adding a resistor R_B in series with every base lead, find the worst-case conditions for fan-out. Assume for simplicity of analysis that all transistors in the circuit are identical, and specifically, that all have identical input characteristics. Also, assume a fixed turn-on overdrive factor n. The spread of each element value and voltage is given in Table P7.1 below.

TABLE P7.1

Variable	Value		
	Minimum	Nominal	Maximum
V_{CC}	2.7 volts	3	3.3
R_L	900 ohms	1000	1100
β_F	25	50	75
Logic level "0"	−1 volt	0	+0.2
Logic level "1"	+2.5 volts	+3	+3.3
R_1	900 ohms	1000	1100

P7.4 Extend the fan-in discussion in Sec. 7.4.1 by calculating an expression for $V_{BE}(P)$ in Fig. 7.14 which is similar in form to Eq. 7.28. Discuss the effect of fan-in on voltage margin Δ_L in this case.

Index